HOUGHTON MIFFLIN

Reading

A Legacy of Literacy

Nature's Fury

THEME 1

Nature's Fury

Reader's Library Selection 1, *Riding Out the Storm*
To accompany Anthology Selection 1, *Earthquake Terror*
Comprehension Skill: Sequence of Events

Reader's Library Selection 2, *White Dragon: Anna Allen in the Face of Danger*
To accompany Anthology Selection 2, *Eye of the Storm: Chasing Storms with Warren Faidley*
Comprehension Skill: Text Organization

Reader's Library Selection 3, *Floods*
To accompany Anthology Selection 3, *Volcanoes*
Comprehension Skill: Categorize/Classify

Riding Out the Storm

by Kathryn Snyder
illustrated by Karen Chandler

Riding Out the Storm

by Kathryn Snyder
illustrated by Karen Chandler

Strategy Focus

Raylee is home alone, and a hurricane is on the way! Will she be able to ride out the storm? As you read, try to **predict** what will happen next.

Responding

Think About the Selection

1 What kind of storm hits Raylee's town?

2 What does "riding out a storm" mean?

3 What are the first three things that Raylee does after Aunt Luelle leaves?

Sequence of Events

Copy this chart on a piece of paper. Fill in the events. Then complete charts like this one for the other parts of the story.

Part of story: Where's Aunt Luelle?			
Event 1	**Event 2**	**Event 3**	**Event 4**
Raylee wakes up.	She talks to Momma on the phone.	?	?

4

25

"Here! Here!" she yelled.

The people in the helicopter saw her! The helicopter headed toward her. She waved her hands over her head.

Before long, a rescuer was being lowered from the helicopter. Soon Raylee and Chomper would be safe.

She had made it through a hurricane — all alone. She had been able to ride out the storm.

Where's Aunt Luelle?

Raylee looked out the window. The sky was gray and ashy. It looked the color of the Gulf of Mexico waters. Raylee could see huge waves in the distance. It sure looked like a storm was coming.

Raylee's parents had taped the windows last night. They hadn't thought the wooden shutters were needed. But the storm watch of last night had become a hurricane warning in the past two hours. People who lived in low-lying areas were heading for the shelters. That's just what Raylee was going to do — head for the shelter. She'd go the minute that Aunt Luelle came by.

Momma had called from work around ten and told Raylee, "I'll try to pick you up at noon. If I can't do it, Aunt Luelle will. She'll be by at one o'clock. We'll meet at the shelter. We have plenty of time. The storm won't really hit until later this afternoon."

Well, Momma hadn't come at noon. It was nearly one. Drops of rain splattered against the window, leaving spots the size of quarters. *Where are you, Aunt Luelle?* Raylee thought. *Chomper and I are waiting.* Raylee suddenly froze. Where was that dog?

6

Raylee looked above her. The early morning light was coming through the metal roof vent above her. She began to pull at it. She needed something hard to hit it with. All she had was the flashlight. It would have to work.

Raylee held the flashlight at one end. She pounded against the vent with all her might. The vent began to move. In just a few minutes, the vent was off.

Raylee pounded at the wood and shingles. Soon the hole was big enough for Raylee to push her head and shoulders through. A gentle rain was now falling.

23

Through the Roof!

Hour after hour, Raylee and Chomper waited. Would the winds never die down? The flashlight ran out. All Raylee could do was sit in the dark and wait. Every so often, she would fall asleep.

Towards morning, something woke Raylee from one of her cat naps. It was the sound of a helicopter right above the house. Rescue! But how could Raylee let the rescuers know where she was?

Storms always upset Chomper. "Chomper!" Raylee called. "Chomper. Come here! *Now!*" There was no sign of the dog.

Raylee walked through the house. She looked under beds and in closets. Then, glancing out the kitchen window, she saw Chomper by the fence. "Come back, right now!" Raylee yelled. Chomper wouldn't come.

Raylee dashed out into the rain. Chomper darted around the corner. He disappeared into the next yard. Raylee fought through the wind, looking for her lost mutt. She finally spotted him under the neighbor's porch.

22

7

It took Raylee nearly twenty minutes to get him out. At one point, Raylee thought she heard a car horn. But the wind made things sound strange. So, she didn't think it was Aunt Luelle. Finally she got Chomper to crawl close enough that she could grab his collar.

Raylee dragged Chomper back into the house just in time to see Aunt Luelle drive off. "No!" she screamed. She ran outside and waved at the car. But Aunt Luelle didn't see her. *She must have thought I went with Momma,* Raylee realized.

Raylee could see the late afternoon sunlight on the water below. The water was now halfway up the hallway walls. She could go down there and swim. But the water looked so dirty. There were probably snakes in it too. Raylee decided to stay where she was.

Soon the quiet ended. The wind blew wildly against the roof again. Except for the flashlight's light, everything was dark now. A square metal roof vent clattered under the pounding rain.

The roof shook harder, harder, and even harder. Raylee prayed that the wind would not lift the roof, her, and Chomper into the dark sky.

8

21

Storm Power

Raylee slammed the door behind her. "Bad dog!" she yelled at Chomper. Then Raylee knelt to hug him. "I know," Raylee said gently. "You were just scared." Saying the word *scared* sent a chill up Raylee's neck. What would she do now?

Raylee changed into dry clothes. Then she turned on the TV in the kitchen. The news showed people in a shelter. She wondered if she'd see Momma or Aunt Luelle.

20

Riding It Out

When she turned to fill a plastic bottle with water, Raylee heard a noise. SNAP! The TV screen went gray. The refrigerator stopped humming too.

The power was out. Raylee grabbed the phone. But when she punched in 9-1-1, there was silence. The phone was dead too.

The kitchen window streamed with water. Through it, Raylee could see trees bending helplessly in the wind. The storm was starting to get much worse.

Well, Raylee decided, *I'll just have to ride the storm out.* That's what Aunt Luelle always said — *ride the storm out.* It meant making do until the storm was over — all by herself.

Raylee sat, leaning against the wall. Chomper sat right beside her. The rain sounded like a thousand drummers. It beat above their heads for hours.

Then suddenly it was quiet. *The eye of the storm,* Raylee thought. She knew that was the middle of the storm, where everything was calm. But it would only be quiet for a short time.

10

19

Aunt Luelle had told her how in 1961 a neighbor's roof had blown right off.

Please, roof, stay put, Raylee thought.

18

11

The two of them sat at the edge of the attic opening. Below them was a dark, noisy, dirty river of water. Raylee flashed her flashlight over the surface. She thought she saw a dead fish.

The attic was tiny. But at least it was dry — for now. But Raylee knew that an attic was exactly the wrong place to be during a hurricane.

12

17

Raylee jumped up. The water was at her ankles, then her knees. It was rising higher!

She pushed out of the bathroom into the hallway. Chairs and tables floated and crashed everywhere.

With a mighty jump, Raylee reached the handle to the attic door. She used every bit of strength to pull the door down. She ran up the stairs and called to Chomper to follow.

Aunt Luelle never forgot riding out Hurricane Carla back in 1961. She said it was the scariest experience of her life. She also said she'd make sure no family member ever rode out another hurricane. *But hadn't Aunt Luelle just driven off and left me to ride this storm out alone?* Raylee thought.

The wind shrieked like a wild animal. Water poured over the sides of the roof. Raylee sat on a chair in the living room. She had a flashlight and a bottle of water with her. Chomper lay at her feet. He lifted his head now and then to cry.

The pictures shook on the walls.

16

13

Water and Wind

Raylee squinted to see through the window. The street had turned into a river. The driveway was like a lake. Water was roaring against the front door.

Raylee walked away from the window. Suddenly, the wind blew it out with a BOOM.

Chomper howled. Raylee grabbed his collar and led him into the bathroom. The bathroom was the safest place to be. Its pipes were fixed to the earth. Raylee sat under the sink and and held Chomper. The wind whistled through the plumbing. WHOOOO! WHOOOO!

Then came horrible noises of the front door cracking apart. Water was pouring into the house! It was coming into the bathroom!

14

15

12A

White Dragon:
Anna Allen in the Face of Danger

by Maryann Dobeck
illustrations by Todd Leonardo

White Dragon:

Anna Allen in the Face of Danger

by Maryann Dobeck
illustrations by Todd Leonardo

Strategy Focus

Anna Allen loved the snow. She never dreamed it would almost kill her. As you read, think of **questions** about the story that you want answered.

26

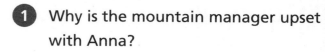
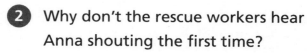

Responding

Think About the Selection

1 Why is the mountain manager upset with Anna?

2 Why don't the rescue workers hear Anna shouting the first time?

3 How do the headings help you read the story?

Using Headings

Make a chart like this on a piece of paper. For every heading in the story, write what that part of the story tells about.

Heading	This part of the story tells about...
Mountains of Snow	The Sierra Nevada mountains where Anna Allen works
Blasting the Slopes	?
Buried Alive	?
Searchers Start Looking	?
Bridget the Rescue Dog	?
Days Under Snow	?

47

14A

Today Anna Allen works at the Mammoth Mountain Ski Resort in California. She visits schools and teaches ski safety. She tells of the five days in March 1982 when she was trapped by an avalanche. She hopes her story will help others know the fury of the White Dragon.

46

Mountains of Snow

In 1982, it snowed hard in the Sierra Nevada, a chain of mountains in California. By late March, the mountains lay beneath a deep cover of snow. Business was booming for the ski resorts there. All day long, skiers rode up the mountainsides and skied down the smooth white slopes.

2

Skiers fly down the slopes of Alpine Meadows, overlooking Lake Tahoe.

Alpine Meadows

SIERRA NEVADA

Lake Tahoe

Anna Allen worked at the Alpine Meadows Ski Resort near Lake Tahoe. She ran the chair lift that takes skiers up the mountains so that they can ski down. It was a good job for a 22-year-old woman who loved the outdoors. She loved skiing. And every day, she could look at some of the most beautiful mountains in the world.

28

The White Dragon

There is an old riddle that is told in snow country. It goes like this: *What flies without wings, hits without hands, and sees without eyes?* The answer is a *White Dragon*. It's another name for an avalanche.

People look over the damage done by a White Dragon.

45

16A

Back on the Slopes

At the hospital, Anna was in very bad shape. Her legs had been in the cold for too long. In the end, she lost her right leg below the knee and all the toes on her left foot.

Anna learned to walk with an artificial leg. She refused to feel sorry for herself. Within a year, she was back skiing. Nearly a year after the avalanche, she entered a race for disabled skiers. "I've got to keep going," she said.

44

On the last day of March, Anna awoke to a fresh layer of snow. It was six feet deep in some places. Throughout the day, heavy wet snow continued to fall. Anna wanted to help a friend dig out his car from under the snow. She needed her waterproof ski pants. They were in a locker at the ski resort. Anna set off for the resort to get them.

29

When steep slopes can hold no more snow, the snow begins to slide. Some avalanches reach speeds of 200 miles per hour.

30

43

"Anna, is that you?" the searchers yelled down.

"Of course it is!" she called back weakly.

Anna grabbed a searcher's hand. He pulled. She crawled up into daylight. It had taken five long, cold days, but now she was free!

A helicopter carrying Anna lifted off while the rescuers cheered.

Blasting the Slopes

The mountain manager was in charge of making things safe for skiers at the resort. He had closed the resort that day. He knew that the heavy snow might slide down the slopes and become an avalanche. Without warning, tons of snow could come crashing down the mountainside. An avalanche could snap trees, smash buildings, and bury skiers.

The locker room was in a three-story building near the ski lodge. As Anna went into the building, she met the mountain manager. He seemed upset with her.

He told Anna that she had just done something foolish and dangerous. "You skied on the main road!" he pointed out. A team was getting ready to blast the snow on that road. Anna had just missed getting caught in the blasting.

42

31

Skilled blasters help prevent large avalanches.

Trained workers blast the slopes to make small avalanches. Setting off a few small avalanches can stop big avalanches from happening. Big avalanches can be deadly.

But getting caught in an area being blasted can be deadly too. Anna had not known about the blasting. She had been very lucky to miss it.

Search and Rescue

Snow fell heavily for two more days. Then the skies cleared. The searchers began their work again.

Bridget sniffed again at the spot above Anna. Again, she barked. Someone was down there. This time, the searchers stayed. They began digging. They dug deeper and deeper until they hit a board. They pulled the board away to find a hand reaching up through the snow.

32

41

Buried Alive

Anna knew how lucky she had been. If she had known they were blasting the slopes, she never would have gone to the lodge. She hurried to the hall lined with lockers. She would just grab her ski pants and head home.

CRASH! Suddenly something hard hit her. Everything went black.

Anna knew that another avalanche might happen at any time. Maybe that was why the searchers had moved away. "I would hate to have someone else die trying to find me," she thought.

Anna had nothing to eat but snow. She felt weak from hunger and cold. She worried that she might pass out before the searchers came again. If she fell asleep for too long, she could easily die. She fought to stay awake.

40

33

21A

When Anna awoke, she had trouble thinking clearly. Her head hurt terribly. She looked around, but she didn't know where she was. At first she thought she was at home. She thought that maybe the hot water heater had blown up. Or maybe there had been an earthquake. Slowly her thoughts became clearer. "An avalanche," she realized.

Anna could feel the wooden lockers that had fallen against a bench to form a space. The space was only about three feet wide and five feet long. She could not see. It was as dark as night and as cold as a refrigerator. There was little room for her to move. Anna was not sure that she would leave this place alive.

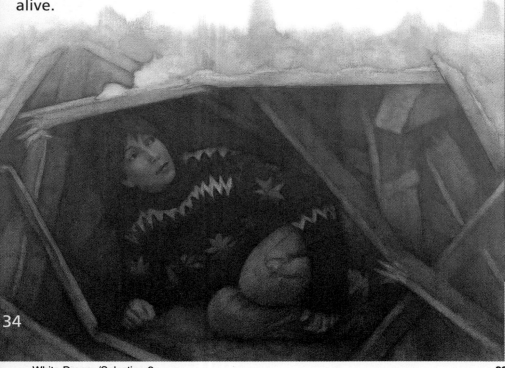

34

39

Days Under Snow

While the people above looked for Anna, she fought for her life as best as she could. She had found some matches. Their light helped her find warm clothing in the lockers. It hurt to move her body, but she pulled on several layers. Still she shivered from the cold. Her teeth chattered. Could she stay warm enough for long enough?

In the darkness, Anna heard a dog barking. The sound came from above her. A rescue dog! Anna shouted and shouted. "I'm here! I'm down here!" But the dog's barking soon stopped. She heard the sounds of people moving away. In deep snow, sounds easily travel down, but not up. She realized that the rescuers must not have heard her.

Searchers Start Looking

A large avalanche had rushed down from the slopes above. It had smashed the building to pieces before coming to a stop in a nearby parking lot.

A lucky man at one end of the building was able to dig himself out. Searchers were already on the scene. How many other people might be buried in the building and under the snow?

Two searchers had seen Anna walk toward another part of the building. That part of the lodge looked completely destroyed. It didn't seem possible that anyone there could have survived. They would try looking there later. For now, searchers chose a different spot to hunt in.

38

35

Rescue workers and dogs search for people buried under the snow.

Bridget the Rescue Dog

Later the next day, the search moved back to the building where Anna was trapped. The searchers brought in specially trained rescue dogs. These dogs are trained to find buried people by sniffing the snow. Then they help the searchers dig the people out of the snow.

On the third day, a rescue dog named Bridget barked loudly. Someone was buried! Bridget stood over the spot where Anna lay trapped. Several searchers listened for someone below. But they couldn't hear anything.

It had begun to snow heavily again. The dogs and the rescue workers couldn't keep looking. For the time being, the search had to be called off.

Selection 3

FLOODS

by Barbara Brooks Simons

FLOODS

by Barbara Brooks Simons

Strategy Focus

In this selection, you'll read about two types of floods. **Monitor** your reading to make sure you understand each type. Reread parts to **clarify** anything you don't understand.

48

Responding

Think About the Selection

1. What is the most common type of flood?

2. Why are floods so dangerous?

3. What are the two main kinds of floods?

Categorize It and Classify It

You can use a diagram like this to keep track of the two kinds of floods that you read about. Copy the diagram on a piece of paper and complete it. Then complete another diagram for *river floods*.

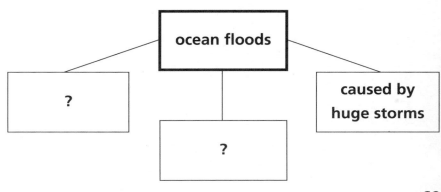

ocean floods

?

?

caused by huge storms

69

SOME BIG FLOODS IN AMERICAN HISTORY

1861	Floods rise along rivers on the Pacific coast, from Oregon to southern California.
1889	The Johnstown Flood kills 2,200 people.
1900	Hurricane and floods in Galveston, Texas kill 6,000 people.
1913	Floods hit the Ohio River valley; about 465 people are killed.
1927	Rainstorms cause floods on the lower Mississippi, killing 313 people.
1928	The St. Francis Dam, near Los Angeles, breaks; about 400 people die.
1938	Hurricane and ocean storm cause floods in New England; 600 people die.
1972	Flash floods hit Rapid City, South Dakota. Hurricane Agnes causes flash floods in New York and Pennsylvania.
1993	Floods hit nine states in the Midwest; 50 people die.
1997	The Red River causes floods in North Dakota.

People have lived near water throughout time. Being near a river or ocean can make life easier. Rivers give people water for drinking, swimming, and growing crops. Rivers and oceans give people food, such as fish and water birds. People also use rivers and oceans for boat travel.

Ancient Egyptians depended on the Nile River for food, travel, and water for crops.

But living near water can also be dangerous. The greatest danger comes from floods. In the United States, about 20 million people live in places where floods are likely.

Moving water can be very strong. Flood waters knock down trees and carry away houses. Towns can be lost. People and animals can drown.

What can people do to stop floods? Dams and levees can help hold back water to stop river floods. People can also dig canals to help carry away flood water. Building homes farther from rivers and oceans also can cut down on damage. Sometimes all people can do is try to escape nature's fury.

Flood waters tipped this house and sent a tree through a second-floor window in Johnstown, PA in 1889.

A riverboat moves down the Mississippi River.

50

67

28A

Frightened Hawaiians run from tsunami waters in Kilauea in 1960.

A farm in Iowa is covered by flood waters in 1998.

More tsunamis have hit Hawaii than any other part of the United States. In the past 100 years, there have been 13 big tsunamis in Hawaii. Waves have reached as high as 55 feet. Tsunamis hit Hawaii after a big earthquake in 1975. Campers at Volcanoes National Park woke up when the ground started moving. They could hardly stand up. Thirty seconds later, the first tsunami wave hit land. Two campers drowned, and 19 others were hurt.

Ocean floods are caused by very big storms or other unusual events, such as earthquakes. In the United States, river floods are much more common. Why do they happen? The easiest answer is, "Too much water."

66

51

River floods can happen at any time. They are more likely in late winter and early spring. Heavy rain or melting snow can make streams or rivers overflow onto the land and cover fields and roads. Frozen ground can't soak up all the water.

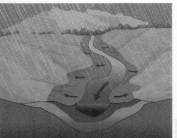

Left: Too much water from rain or snow can cause a river to overflow its banks.

Below: Rain causes high waters in this Louisiana swamp.

In some parts of the world, earthquakes can make huge ocean waves, called *tsunamis* (su-NAM-ees). They are most common in the Pacific Ocean. A tsunami moves quickly across the sea, at speeds of up to 500 miles an hour. When the wave hits the land, it turns into a giant wall of water. It can be over 50 feet high. It smashes over houses on shore and causes serious trouble.

Tsunami waters blast the coast of Hawaii in 1960.

52

65

Ice is another problem. Sometimes ice blocks the water in a river. The water stops moving. Tons of water build up behind the ice, flooding the land upstream. When the ice melts, water moves downstream very quickly and causes more flooding.

Left: Ice blocking a river causes water to overflow the river's banks.

Below: Ice covers the Mississippi River.

Heavy rains from hurricanes also cause sudden floods away from the seacoast. In June 1972, Hurricane Agnes caused a week of heavy rains. Although the hurricane first hit Florida, the heavy rain hit all along the East Coast. Rivers flooded in Virginia, New York, and Pennsylvania. Roaring water pushed houses out of the ground. The water knocked cars around like toys and smashed boats to pieces. The storm killed more than 100 people and left 250,000 without homes.

Flood waters from Hurricane Agnes cover a Pennsylvania town.

The Hoover Dam was built on the Colorado River in the 1930s. It holds back enough water to cover the entire state of Pennsylvania with one foot of water!

Too much water can also make dams break. Dams are giant walls made to block water and control how it flows. They often hold back tons of water. When dams break, the flood is quick and deadly.

Today, people know how to build safe, strong dams. But not long ago, many dams were just piles of dirt. They were not very safe.

Hurricanes often happen in late summer and early fall. These are dangerous storms that begin in the warm waters of the Caribbean Sea. They usually reach land in the southeast United States or the Gulf of Mexico.

Hurricanes often bring winds of 100 miles an hour or more. These strong winds whip up high waves that wash over the land. They smash into beach homes and towns.

Above: The arrows show the directions that hurricanes usually travel.

Left: A truck plows through flood waters in Cape Hatteras, North Carolina.

54

63

Hurricane winds and rain pound the East Coast in these two photos.

Floods also happen near the ocean. In the United States, floods near the ocean are mostly caused by huge storms or hurricanes. In other places, they may happen when an earthquake hits under the ocean.

The Mississippi is the largest river in the United States. It moves through a wide valley down the center of the country. There have always been floods along the Mississippi. In many places, people have made walls of earth or concrete along the river's banks. These walls are called *levees*. Levees help block water from coming onto the land.

Above: The Mississippi River flood plain in Iowa is covered with flood water.

Right: The flat land on either side of a river is the flood plain.

62

55

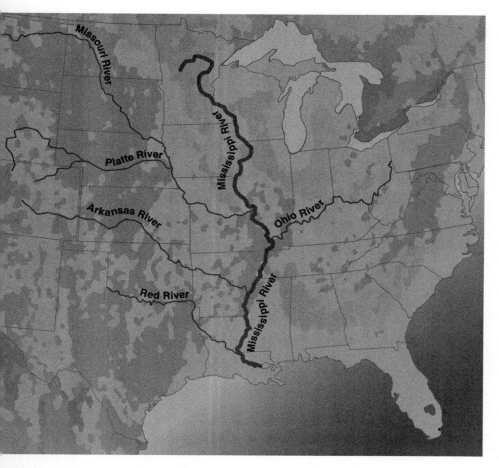

The Mississippi River runs through the center of the United States. A number of other big rivers flow into the Mississippi.

The Mississippi River gets its water from a large part of the United States. Hundreds of smaller rivers send water into the Mississippi.

The water grew to 70 feet high. It picked up trees and houses. It knocked down bridges and train tracks. In just minutes, the flood reached Johnstown.

There was no warning. The water smashed into the town. It washed away factories, stores, and houses. Then it raced down the valley and covered other small towns. More than 2,000 people died in the Johnstown Flood. It took a long time for life to return to how it had been. Because of the flood, new laws were passed to make dams safer.

The flood waters in Johnstown blasted through buildings, smashing them to bits.

56

61

34A

Flood waters hit Johnstown hard on May 31, 1889.

A photographer guides a boat across Mississippi flood waters that covered this farm in 1993.

The worst flood to hit America happened when a dam fell down. Johnstown, Pennsylvania is in a small valley in the Allegheny Mountains. There used to be an old dam about 15 miles above the town on the Little Conemaugh (CON-em-ah) River. No one had fixed it in many years. In the spring of 1889, heavy rains began. At Johnstown, the river rose and covered some streets.

By the next morning, the lake behind the dam was full. Later that day the dam fell from the weight of the water. A huge wave rushed down the narrow valley.

Some years are worse for floods than others. In the Midwest, people will not forget 1993. Winter snows and spring rain had soaked the ground. In June, more rain began. It fell week after week. The ground couldn't soak it up. So water began to move onto the land all along the Mississippi.

60

57

The levees could not hold back the water. People rushed to pile up bags of sand, but water moved over fields and washed into houses. The worst floods along the Mississippi were in Iowa, Missouri, and Illinois. From the air, Iowa looked like a huge lake. In all, the floods hit 12,000 square miles in nine states. About 70,000 people lost their homes. Fifty people lost their lives.

Missouri residents use sandbags to build up a levee in July, 1993.

58

59

HOUGHTON MIFFLIN

Reading

A Legacy of Literacy

Give It All You've Got

THEME 2

Give It All You've Got

Reader's Library Selection 1, *Meet Yo-Yo Ma*
To accompany Anthology Selection 1, *Michelle Kwan: My Story — Heart of a Champion*
Comprehension Skill: Fact and Opinion

Reader's Library Selection 2, *Victor Sews*
To accompany Anthology Selection 2, *La Bamba*
Comprehension Skill: Story Structure

Reader's Library Selection 3, *Falling off a Log*
To accompany Anthology Selection 3, *The Fear Place*
Comprehension Skill: Predicting Outcomes

Reader's Library Selection 4, *Buck Leonard: Baseball's Greatest Gentleman*
To accompany Anthology Selection 4, *Mae Jemison: Space Scientist*
Comprehension Skill: Topic/Main Idea

Meet Yo-Yo Ma

by Meish Goldish

1B

Meet *Yo-Yo Ma*
by Meish Goldish

Strategy Focus

How did Yo-Yo Ma become one of the finest musicians of our time? As you read, be sure to **evaluate** the facts and the opinions about this famous cello player.

Responding

Think About the Selection

1 Why do you think Yo-Yo Ma's cello playing changes after he moves to New York?

2 What does Yo-Yo Ma mean when he says, "When your brain and heart are engaged, you can't go wrong"?

3 Give one example each of a fact and an opinion in the story.

Fact and Opinion

Copy this chart on a piece of paper. Write whether each sentence is a fact or an opinion.

Clue	Fact or Opinion?
Yo-Yo Ma is among the finest cello players in the world.	?
Yo-Yo Ma's father was his first teacher.	?

25

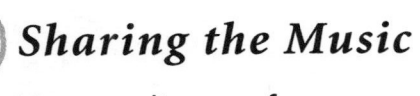

Sharing the Music

Most audiences for classical music are older adults, especially in the United States. But Yo-Yo Ma wanted young people to learn to enjoy the works of great composers. He remembered the joy of growing up in a home filled with music. That's how he wanted his children to grow up.

Yo-Yo began appearing with his cello on children's television programs such as *Sesame Street* and *Mister Rogers' Neighborhood*. Maybe children who had never heard a cello before would feel its beauty.

Yo-Yo's older sister was learning to play the violin. Yo-Yo was only four years old. He tried the violin too. But he decided that he wanted a different stringed instrument — a bigger one. He wanted a cello. Yo-Yo needed help just to hold the cello. "I had to sit up on three telephone books, and there was always trouble finding the right size chair," he later remembered.

22

7

5B

Isaac Stern

Yo-Yo's father was his first teacher. Mr. Ma gave his son difficult music to play. It was written by the great composer Johann Sebastian Bach (YO-haan Seb-AST-shun Bah-k). Mr. Ma told Yo-Yo to learn just a little bit at a time. Every day, Yo-Yo learned a little more than the day before.

By the time he was five, Yo-Yo could play some of the Bach works by heart. He was performing at the University of Paris. In the audience was a famous violinist, Isaac Stern. Stern told people that Yo-Yo Ma's talent was "extraordinary."

Yo-Yo liked playing the cello. More importantly, he was starting to love great classical music.

Yo-Yo Ma decided to cut back on his performing dates. He was determined to pay as much attention to his family as he did to playing cello. He never regretted his decision.

Yo-Yo Ma performs with the Mark Morris Dance Company in Boston, MA.

8

21

Yo-Yo went ahead with the operation. Fortunately, the operation was a complete success. And although Yo-Yo Ma's upper body was in a cast for six months, he still practiced the cello. He was determined that his life in music would go on.

Once Yo-Yo had fully recovered, he got busier than ever. Yo-Yo Ma couldn't say no when someone asked for just one more concert in a city. It was hard for him to turn down exciting chances to play for people. But Yo-Yo also knew he was needed at home, now more than ever. In 1984 he and Jill had a son. Two years later, the family grew again when their daughter was born.

Johann Sebastian Bach

20

9

Growing up in New York City

When Yo-Yo was seven, the family left France to live in New York City.

In New York, Yo-Yo's new music teacher saw that the young cellist was remarkably gifted. Yo-Yo performed on television when he was eight. He gave a concert at Carnegie Hall when he was nine. That same year, he entered the Juilliard School of Music. It is one of the finest music schools in the world.

But Yo-Yo's new, busy life came to a sudden stop. When he was 25, Yo-Yo faced a serious health problem. He had something wrong with his back, called a curved spine. It was now giving him great pain. His doctors told him he needed to have an operation to fix it. It had to be done while his body was still young. If he waited too long, the operation might not work.

There was another, scarier risk. The doctors told Yo-Yo that the operation might harm his nerves. If that happened, Yo-Yo might never be able to play the cello again.

Still, Yo-Yo kept a positive attitude. He told Jill, "If I come out of this alive but not able to have control of my fingers, I will have had a very fulfilling life in music."

10

19

8B

Overcoming Trouble

Yo-Yo Ma married Jill Hornor in 1978. His career was growing quickly now. He was being invited to give concerts all over the world. He traveled nearly every week of the year. When he wasn't performing, he was making recordings. He didn't get home as often as he had wanted. So, it got harder and harder for him and Jill to see each other.

Yo-Yo was very small and shy. He had been taught to obey his parents quietly and without question. Now, in the United States, his music teacher wanted him to show his feelings more. At school, he was supposed to speak up. American children were expected to ask lots of questions about everything.

Yo-Yo Ma felt torn. How could he fit in with other American kids and still be a good son?

Yo-Yo continued to study music. His cello playing began to change. It felt freer, more full of feeling.

Carnegie Hall

18

11

A Big Decision

Yo-Yo Ma had been performing in public since early childhood. Then, at the age of seventeen, he faced a choice. Should he try to earn a living as a performer? Or should he get a college education? Yo-Yo Ma chose college.

Yo-Yo Ma was learning to draw on something deep inside himself to share with listeners. It was more than talent or skill. It was the special quality that made truly great musicians. He was learning how to make the cello come alive with feelings. He was learning to show the fear, dreaminess, joy, hope, and sorrow that live in the music.

"When your brain and heart are engaged, you can't go wrong," Yo-Yo Ma later said. And by the time Yo-Yo left Harvard, he seldom did go wrong.

12

17

In 1998, Yo-Yo Ma played in a celebration in Washington, D.C. It was to honor the music of J. S. Bach.

16

At Harvard University, Yo-Yo Ma studied more than music. He explored literature and history and other subjects. He learned to form his own ideas about the things he was studying in class.

Harvard University in Cambridge, MA

13

Yo-Yo Ma has said that choosing an education was the "best decision" he ever made. It gave him more choices in life. He knew he could have a career outside of music if he wished to someday. He said, "It's not that I'm stuck playing the cello because it's the only thing I can do."

Yo-Yo Ma performs at Carnegie Hall.

Becoming a Great Cellist

At Harvard, Yo-Yo Ma continued to perform and to learn about music. Cellists must know how to use their fingers and the bow in just the right way. Yo-Yo Ma had developed plenty of skills for the cello since his childhood. He had learned from great teachers. He regularly practiced for long hours. But as Yo-Yo Ma grew older, he was learning more than skills.

14

15

Victor Sews

by Lee S. Justice
illustrated by Joe Cepeda

Victor Sews

by Lee S. Justice
illustrated by Joe Cepeda

Strategy Focus

Is sewing class too hard for Victor? As you read, stop and **summarize** each part of the story.

Responding

Think About the Selection

1. Why does Victor have a weird dream?

2. How does Victor's mistake turn out to be a good thing?

3. What is Victor's problem in the story?

Story Structure

Copy this simple story map on a piece of paper and complete it.

Story Map for *Victor Sews*	
Main Character: Victor	
Settings: 1. sewing class	**2.** Victor's home
Problem:	?
Beginning:	?
Middle:	?
End:	?

Whatever Carmen does, a lot of other kids do. Soon the school was filled with kids wearing pants like mine.

I told my mother what happened. "Everyone is wearing the pants," I said. "They even call them *Victors*."

My mother just nodded her head in a knowing way. "Uncle Oscar would be so proud," she said.

It was the first day of sewing class. Ms. Lee was telling us about the pants we'd be making. "Keisha and Thomas are wearing the pants they made last term," said Ms. Lee.

Keisha and Thomas stood at the front of the room to model their pants. They looked like they wanted to be somewhere else. But the pants weren't bad.

"They're like pajama pants," Ms. Lee went on. "But they're for everyday wear. I think it's important for kids to make something they can actually wear and be proud of."

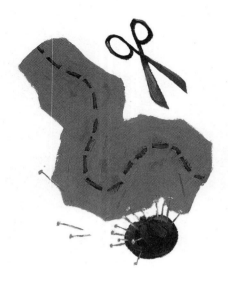

I liked the idea of sewing. But that was before I tried it.

First of all, we had to iron our paper patterns. The patterns were like the plans for making the pants.

"Victor," Ms. Lee said to me, "may I suggest that you spread out the pattern more smoothly?"

I looked around. Everybody else's patterns were smooth. My patterns were wrinkled. There were even a few rips.

"Oops," I said.

I entered the room strutting. There were roars and shrieks of laughter. I took a few bows.

When the laughter quieted down, I heard Nina's voice. "Look at how Victor matched up the designs on the front and back. They're *almost* the same. That's so artistic."

"Actually, those pants are cool," said Carmen.

I looked closely at their faces. Were they kidding?

Ms. Lee smiled at me. "You're a style maker, Victor," she said

A few days later, Carmen showed up in pants she had sewn at home. The front and the back didn't match. One leg was a little longer than the other.

That's when I noticed that the front and the back had different designs. One leg ended just below the knee. The other ended at the ankle. I thought about running away.

"Well, if I look like a clown, I may as well act like one," I told myself.

30

43

"Is your sewing class still good?" Mom asked me that night.

"It's OK," I answered. "The best part about it is that it's almost over."

The last step was hemming the pant legs. I was supposed to do that by hand. But I thought the machine would do it faster. That was mistake number two zillion. It did go fast — too fast. Before I knew it, I had hemmed one leg shut.

I tried picking the thread out of the cloth. After ten minutes, I had picked out three stitches. If I kept up at that pace, I'd be done in about two years.

"I'll just cut and hem again," I decided quickly.

On the last day of sewing class, we were each supposed to parade around the room in our new pants. I put on my pants and looked in the bathroom mirror.

Next we were supposed to pin the patterns to the cloth we had picked out. Mine was black with little yellow squares and triangles on it. "That's a nice design," Nina said to me.

Nina is a girl I've liked for a long time. So her compliment made me feel good. I kept pinning, trying to come up with something nice to say back.

The next thing I knew, Ms. Lee was beside me. "Victor," she said, "remember what I said about pinning to the other side of the fabric? The side that will be the outside of the pants."

I saw that I had laid down the cloth the wrong way. Everybody else's cloth *was* pinned on the outside. How come nobody but me had a problem?

I pulled out the pins, flipped the cloth over, and started pinning again. I worked fast.

42

31

"Victor," said Ms. Lee a short while later. "Do you really need *that* many pins?" I looked down. Sure enough, about a million pins were sticking out of my pattern paper. What could I have been thinking?

Carmen pointed at my work. "Victor's making porcupine pants," she said.

I made a goofy face, pretending to be surprised by all those pins. Everybody laughed.

"There should be more in the box," said Ms. Lee, pointing me to the fabric rolls. "Remember to do all the steps in the right order, Victor."

I grabbed the fabric, spread it out, cut, and began pinning the pattern. I worked so fast that I felt like a real pro. "I bet this is how Uncle Oscar did it," I thought. I pictured the Yankees at my shoulder, admiring my skill.

I didn't notice it at the time, but this cloth did not exactly match the cloth for the front of my pants. This one was yellow with big black squares and triangles.

Why didn't I notice the difference?

32

41

"How's that sewing class going?" Mom asked me a few weeks later.

"OK," I said.

"It's good that boys take sewing these days," Mom said. "When I went to school, boys took wood shop, and girls took sewing. I'm glad those days are over. Things are more fair now. Who knows? Maybe you'll have the talent of my uncle Oscar."

"Who's he?" I asked my mother.

"My grandmother's brother. He was a tailor. He even made suits for the Yankees."

"He sewed the Yankees' uniforms?" I asked.

40

33

"No, their *suits* — the clothes they wore off the field" said Mom. "Some of the ballplayers would come to Uncle Oscar's shop to get their suits tailored. He did good work. I took you to his shop once when you were very small. I guess you don't remember."

That night I had a weird dream. I dreamed I was playing for the Yankees. But I couldn't move right because my uniform didn't fit. Every time I swung the bat, I heard the sound of cloth ripping.

When I woke up, the sheets and blankets were tightly wrapped around me.

Then I remembered it was Tuesday. Oh, no! Sewing class again.

I saw why it took a whole term to sew a pair of pants. There were so many steps! You had to iron, then pin, then trace, then iron again. It went on and on. When we started, I barely knew what a needle was. Now I knew, but it was not a pretty picture.

Finally, I got the hang of using the machine. The needle poked in and out of the cloth nicely. So what if the seam wasn't exactly straight?

"I need more cloth," I told Ms. Lee. "I messed up a little on the back part." Somehow, my sewing had changed the cloth into a tattered rag.

34

39

Another time, cutting with scissors
gave me trouble. I had cut too much. The
pants looked like they'd fit a four-year-old.
"I'll go on a diet," I said.

When the class laughed, Ms. Lee told
me to stop clowning around.

38

35

I got to sewing class just before the bell. Everyone was already working away.

We practiced on the sewing machines using a small piece of cloth.

I sat down at my machine and slipped the cloth under the needle.

Ms. Lee suddenly appeared at my back. "Slow and steady, Victor," she said. I pushed down the foot pedal. "Slo-o-o-w, Victor, gently, GENTLY, **GENTLY!!**" It was too late. My cloth was a tangled wad. Ms. Lee had to cut it out of the machine with scissors.

Next, I used one of the tracing wheels. The tracing wheel looks like a pizza cutter. You roll it in chalk then you roll it on the cloth around the pattern. It traces out a line.

Once again, Ms Lee spotted me. "Victor," she said. "You're supposed to trace onto the other side of the fabric."

36

37

Falling Off a Log

by Anne Miranda
illustrated by Wayne Alfano

Selection 3

Falling Off a Log

by Anne Miranda
illustrated by Wayne Alfano

Strategy Focus

Can saving someone's life be as easy as falling off a log for Marta? As you read, try to **predict** what Marta will do each step of the way.

Responding

Think About the Selection

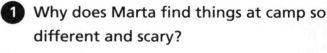
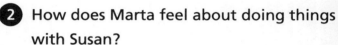

1 Why does Marta find things at camp so different and scary?

2 How does Marta feel about doing things with Susan?

3 What might Susan say to Marta after she hears about how Marta helped Cody?

What Will Happen Next?

Copy this chart. Write two other predictions about what might happen to Marta after the story's ending. Then tell why you think this.

What will happen next when. . .	Why I think this will happen.
Marta crosses back over the bridge: She will walk across and not be as afraid as before.	She finally made it across the bridge. She tells Cody, "It's as easy as falling off a log."
Marta gets back to camp: ?	?
Marta goes on another hike: ?	?

69

26B

68 49

When they got to the log bridge, Cody stopped.

"Can you make it across?" she asked Marta.

Marta smiled and stepped onto the bridge. For some reason, it didn't scare her any more. She thought how proud of her Susan would be. "No problem," she said. "It's as easy as falling off a log."

It had been only two months since Marta had moved to Ohio from Florida. Now she was at summer camp for the first time. She wasn't just away from home. She was away from her new home too! Everything there seemed so different and scary.

When Marta first saw the lake at camp, she stared at the brownish water. It sure wasn't anything like the clear blue water of the beaches back home!

"I'm supposed to swim in that?" she asked Susan. Susan was one of the five girls who shared Cabin 7 with Marta.

"Sure. Why not?" said Susan. Susan was fun and fearless. Marta wished she could be more like her.

"Can you do it?" Marta asked.

Cody couldn't even answer. With her last bit of strength, she gave herself a shot. Then she just lay there for minutes.

Little by little, Cody started to feel better. Finally, she was well enough to start back to camp. Marta and another girl let Cody lean on them to walk.

50

67

When Marta's feet finally landed on solid ground, she ran to the cabin. Cody was lying on an old wooden table. The other girls stood around her. They were all scared.

Cody was having trouble breathing, but she could still talk. "Thanks," she whispered, as Marta handed her the kit.

"Because it's . . . cold and dark!" said Marta.

"Don't worry," said Susan. "You'll get used to it, once you're in."

"But I can't even see what's in the water," said Marta.

"Come on," said Susan. "Swim with me out to the float. It's as easy as falling off a log!"

66

99

51

That's what Susan said about everything. "As easy as falling off a log." Marta had never heard anyone use that saying in Florida.

But Susan had been right. Swimming to the float had been pretty easy. So had canoeing and diving. By the end of the first week, Marta started getting used to life at the lake. And Susan was becoming her best friend. Marta felt like she could do anything with Susan around.

Marta slowly moved forward, inch by inch. When she got to the spot where she had stopped before, she started to back up. "But Cody could die!" she said to herself. "Just don't look at the water." It's what Susan would have said if she were here. Then Marta got down on all fours and slowly crawled across the rest of the bridge.

52

65

That's why Marta agreed to go with Susan on a hike to an old cabin in the woods. Cody, one of the camp counselors, was going with a group of other girls. Marta was excited the morning of the hike. But one look at Susan's face made her excitement instantly disappear.

"I can't go," Susan said. "I don't feel very well. You go. You'll have fun with Cody and the other girls."

"But — " Marta started to say.

Susan read her mind. "Don't worry," she smiled. "It will be as easy as falling off a log."

53

Marta knew what she had to do. She took a deep breath and stepped onto the bridge. It shook as she took her first step. She took a look at the dark marsh water and felt sick. But she had to do it.

64

Marta rushed to the counselors' cabin. Cody was putting things into her backpack.

"Ready to go?" Cody asked.

"Susan's sick," said Marta. "Maybe we should wait another day."

"That's too bad, " Cody said. "But I've got a whole group of campers ready to go. I'll make sure that Nurse Thompson checks in with Susan."

Marta stayed put. She knew what was wrong. Cody must have been stung by a bee! And Cody had left her backpack with the bee sting kit on this side of the bridge.

Marta grabbed Cody's backpack and found the bee sting kit. With the kit in hand, she ran to the edge of the log bridge.

"I've got the bee sting kit," she called out. She hoped one of the other girls would hear her and come get the kit. But there was no answer.

BEE STING
FIRST AID

54

63

32B

Marta felt her stomach turn. "But Susan's my best friend," she started to say. "I do everything with her."

"You'll be fine without her," Cody said.

Marta swallowed and nodded her head.

Cody smiled and threw a few more things into her backpack. One of them was a small plastic box.

Marta nodded and sat down next to Cody's backpack. She was angry with herself. All the other girls had been able to go across. "I'd be able to do it if Susan were here," Marta thought to herself.

Marta figured the group would be back in a couple of minutes. But when fifteen minutes passed she started to get worried. "They better not leave me here," she thought.

Just then she saw Ellen running from behind the cabin. Ellen looked like she was crying.

"It's Cody," Ellen yelled. "She's sick! She can't breathe!"

Ellen ran across the log bridge and headed towards the trail.

"Come on!" Ellen cried. She disappeared down the trail, running full speed to get back to the camp.

62

55

33B

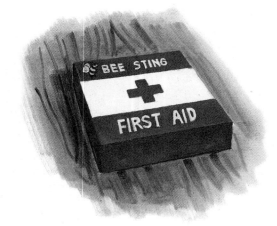

"What's that?" asked Marta.

"My bee sting kit," said Cody. "I'm allergic."

"You're a *what*?" asked Marta. "What's a *lergic*?"

"Not a *lergic*. I'm *allergic*. I have an allergy to bee stings," said Cody. "If I get stung by a bee I could die. I carry this kit all the time. I have to give myself a shot if I get stung."

Cody put on her backpack and headed out the door. Marta followed. They checked in with Nurse Thompson to tell her about Susan. Then they met up with the rest of the group and headed down the trail.

The hike seemed to take forever to Marta. She was tired when Cody finally stopped the group at the edge of a marsh.

"There it is," Cody said, taking off her backpack. She pointed beyond the marsh to the cabin.

56

"Come on, Marta!" said Cody. "You can do it." But Marta wouldn't budge. Finally, Cody gave up.

"It's okay," she said. "I've got to join up with the girls. We'll just take a quick look. You stay there. There are some sandwiches in my backpack if you're hungry."

61

34B

57

60

Marta swallowed and stepped onto the bridge. Her legs felt wobbly. She took six tiny steps and then stopped. She couldn't move another inch.

"I can't!" she gasped.

"Sure you can. It's easier than it looks," said Cody. By this time, Marta wasn't listening. She had already crawled back to the other side.

Ellen Franklin, a girl from Cabin 12, asked, "How do we get there?"

Cody pointed to a thin bridge made of two logs lying side by side. "We just walk across that," she said.

The bridge didn't look safe at all to Marta.

"Ready to go?" Cody said.

Everyone jumped up and headed across the bridge. Marta could feel her stomach spinning like sneakers in a clothes dryer. "I wish Susan was here," she thought. "This really *will* be like falling off a log."

Cody could see that Marta was scared. "I'll go ahead of you to show you how," she said. "It's easy."

Marta watched as Cody slowly walked across the logs behind the other girls. Cody balanced herself like a tightrope walker. Marta didn't want to think about what was swimming in the dark water beneath her.

"Now it's your turn," Cody said when she got to the other side.

58

59

BUCK LEONARD
BASEBALL'S GREATEST GENTLEMAN

by Tyrone Washington

BUCK LEONARD
BASEBALL'S GREATEST GENTLEMAN

by Tyrone Washington

Strategy Focus

You're about to meet one of baseball's great heroes. As you read, **monitor** your reading and reread to **clarify** any parts that aren't clear.

70

Responding

Think About the Selection

1. Why wasn't Buck Leonard as well-known as other baseball stars?

2. How was baseball difficult for teams in the Negro Leagues?

3. Give some supporting details that show that Buck Leonard worked hard off the baseball field too.

Main Idea/Supporting Details

Copy the chart on a piece of paper. Write two details that help support each idea.

Main Idea	Supporting Details
Buck's fans often compared him to Lou Gehrig.	1. Both were polite. 2. ?
Buck Leonard was a tough, hard worker.	1. ? 2. ?

91

Buck Leonard is presented with a plaque honoring his election into the National Baseball Hall of Fame.

In 1972, Buck Leonard finally got the honor he deserved. He was elected to the National Baseball Hall of Fame.

After his playing days were over, Leonard went back to the small southern town where he was born. He had started out life there as a shoeshine boy. He had become one of baseball's great heroes.

Buck Leonard passed away in 1997.

90

Do you know who Buck Leonard was? Chances are you don't. But you probably do know who Ken Griffey Jr. is — if you're any kind of baseball fan at all. You'd also know Griffey if you eat a certain cereal for breakfast every morning. But over fifty years ago, during the 1930s and 1940s, there were no black baseball players on cereal boxes. Back then, African American baseball stars like Buck Leonard were pretty much unknown to most fans.

71

Back in the 1800s, white and black players played on the same baseball teams. But in 1887, the National Association of Baseball Players said black players could no longer play on major league teams. And that was the way it stayed, for many, many years.

Black athletes played baseball in something called the Negro Leagues. In some ways, the Negro Leagues were like the major leagues. There were all-star games and world series. There were also many very talented players. But unlike the players in the major leagues, all the Negro League players were black.

Monte Irvin and Larry Doby were two Negro League stars who crossed over to the major leagues after Jackie Robinson opened the door.

In 1952, Buck Leonard was finally invited to play in the major leagues. But by then he was 45 years old. Buck knew that he couldn't play as well as younger black players. So he said no. He knew that if he played poorly on a major league team, he might hurt other black players' chances of playing in the majors. To the end, Buck was a gentleman and a model of good sportsmanship.

72

89

It wasn't until 1947 that the major leagues hired their first black player, Jackie Robinson. Robinson went to play for the Brooklyn Dodgers, where he became an instant hero to many. He was young and talented. He was able to take insults from people who wanted the league to be all white. Major league officials saw how well Robinson played the game and what a fine sportsman he was. His courage and self-control helped open the door for other black players to come into the major leagues. Little by little, things began to change.

Jackie Robinson was the first African American baseball player to sign a major league contract.

(EAST) NEGRO NATIONAL LEAGUE:

		(WEST) NEGRO AMERICAN LEAGUE
BUCK LEONARD, Homestead Grays	1st Base	PIPER DAVIS, Birmingham Barons
JAMES GILLAM, Baltimore	2nd Base	RAY NEIL, Indianapolis Clowns
THOMAS BUTTS, Baltimore	SS	ART WILSON, Birmingham Barons
ORESTE MINOSO, N. Y. Cubans	3rd Base	HERB SOUELL, Kansas City Monarchs
ROBERT HARVEY, Newark	RF	JOSEPH COLAS, Memphis Red Sox
LUIS MARQUEZ, Homestead Grays	CF	WILLARD BROWN, Kan. City Monarchs
LUCIOUS EASTER, Homestead Grays	LF	CLYDE NELSON, Cleveland Buckeyes
LOUIS LOUDEN, N. Y. Cubans	C	QUINCY TROUPE, Chicago
WILLIAM CASH, Philadelphia Stars	C	SAM HAIRSTON, Indianapolis Clowns
MAXWELL MANNING, Newark	P	CHET BREWER, Cleveland
ROBERT ROMBY, Baltimore	P	BILL POWELL, Birmingham
DAVID BARNHILL, N. Y. Cubans	P	GENTRY JESSOP, Chicago
JOSEPH BLACK, Baltimore	P	BOB LA MARQUE, Kansas City
PAT SCANTLEBURY, N. Y. Cubans	P	LEFTY VERDELL MATHIS, Memphis
	P	JOHNNY WILLIAMS, Clowns
		KING TUT, COACH

— SEE —
LUCIOUS EASTER
who hit a 490-ft. homer into the centerfield bleachers at the Polo Grounds this summer, and other great stars!

Buck Leonard's name sits on top of the Negro National League All Star roster in this poster from 1946.

88

73

Satchel Paige

Oscar Charleston

Negro League players were never as famous as the major league players. But the Negro League had its stars. They were players who were just as good as, and maybe even better than, major league players. There were heroes like Josh Gibson, Satchel Paige, Oscar Charleston — and Buck Leonard.

Buck Leonard was one of the most admired players the Negro League ever had. He was known for his pleasant and easy-going way. He went to bed early, did lots of crossword puzzles, and had a friendly word for everyone. He was also known as one of the greatest gentlemen to ever play baseball.

And on the fields of the Negro Leagues, he made baseball history.

Other players made up some tall tales about Buck Leonard. According to one of his teammates, Buck once hit a home run so far that made it rain. The ball cleared the bleachers, the back fence of the stadium, and several houses. When the ball hit a water tower, it rained for two weeks! These stories were based on Buck's amazing play. They showed just how much other ball players admired him.

In 1938, Buck Leonard almost got a chance at national stardom. He and Josh Gibson were invited into the office of Clark Griffith, who owned the Washington Senators. The Senators were a major league ball club. The two players could hardly sit still. Griffith had heard about how well Leonard and Gibson played. He asked if they would play for him. Of course, they answered yes!

It didn't happen. Griffith argued long and hard to get black players into the majors. But more powerful baseball officials shouted him down. Neither Buck Leonard nor Josh Gibson ever got a major league contract.

74

87

42B

Buck Leonard takes one of his giant home-run swings in 1938.

Buck Leonard in his Homestead Grays uniform

86

75

His full name was Walter Fenner Leonard. But people called him Buck. He was born in 1907 in the small town of Rocky Mount, North Carolina. His father, a railroad brakeman, died of influenza when Buck was a young boy. To support the family, Buck shined shoes at the railway station.

When he was sixteen, Buck worked full-time for a train company. At that early age, he was also a star of his hometown baseball team.

Buck soon began to play professional ball. He played first base for the Homestead Grays of Homestead, Pennsylvania, one of the best Negro League teams. He joined them in 1934.

Buck Leonard finishes one of his many home-run trots around the bases against the Newark Bears in 1943.

76

85

For seventeen seasons, Buck Leonard didn't just play baseball — he *shone*. Buck had one of the highest batting averages ever. To get a batting average, you divide the number of times a player gets a hit by the number of times he's at bat. A 1.000 would be perfect. Most players never hit over .300 in a single season.

Buck Leonard hit .341 over his whole career! In special games against major league teams, Buck hit .382 in all the games combined. That meant he got more hits off major league pitchers than he did off the Negro League pitchers. In 1947 he reached a high point, batting an amazing .410 average for the whole season.

In 1948, when he was 41 years old — old for a professional baseball player — Buck hit .395. Very few baseball players in any league — at any age — have ever hit that well.

The Homestead Grays in 1941. Buck Leonard is kneeling third from left in the front row.

84

77

Lou Gehrig

Buck's fans often compared him to Lou Gehrig, the famous New York Yankees first baseman. Both players were well-known for their polite manner. They were also big, powerful hitters who played in the shadow of even better hitters on their own teams.

Negro League All Stars in 1947

An even bigger problem for Negro League teams was the way the players were treated because they were black. Buck and his teammates were not allowed in most restaurants and hotels when they were on the road. That meant they sometimes had to sleep out on a baseball field or inside the team bus. At sunrise, the Homestead Grays would dust themselves off and get ready to play. But no matter what hardships they faced, Buck Leonard and the rest of Negro League players loved to play the game.

78

83

46B

Babe Ruth   Josh Gibson

Negro League players didn't make as much money as major league players did, and they weren't as well known. During his first season with the Homestead Grays, Buck Leonard made $125 a month — much less than any major league player made. The Homestead Grays, like other Negro League teams, received very little attention in major newspapers. There was little opportunity for Buck to be a well-known, national hero.

Lou Gehrig was not quite as big a slugger as his teammate, Babe Ruth. No matter how hard Lou Gehrig worked, people always seemed to pay more attention to The Babe. Buck Leonard often played as well as his teammate, Josh Gibson. But no matter how well Buck played, Gibson usually stole the show. Gibson always managed to hit more home runs than Buck. He also hit them farther. Yet, like Gehrig, Buck didn't mind being out of the spotlight.

One thing was certain for both pairs of players: They made life hard for opposing teams.

82

79

*Buck Leonard tags out a New York Cubans
baserunner during a game in 1946.*

Buck Leonard was a tough, hard worker who played well, game after game. He once played with a broken hand. He broke it during the first game of a four-game series. Buck just taped up his bad hand and played to the end of the series.

Buck often played as many as three games a day! That's how things were for teams in the Negro Leagues. Major league teams might play double headers — two games in a day. But most of the time, major league players had it pretty easy, playing one game a day.

Buck also worked hard when he wasn't on the baseball field. Since the baseball season didn't last all year long, he'd make money doing different jobs. He might shine shoes or work on the railroad. He'd do whatever he could to support himself until the next baseball season started.

HOUGHTON MIFFLIN

Reading

A Legacy of Literacy

Voices of the Revolution

THEME 3

Voices of the Revolution

Reader's Library Selection 1, *Bunker's Cove*
To accompany Anthology Selection 1, *And Then What Happened, Paul Revere?*
Comprehension Skill: Author's Viewpoint

Reader's Library Selection 2, *The Drummer Boy*
To accompany Anthology Selection 2, *Katie's Trunk*
Comprehension Skill: Cause and Effect

Reader's Library Selection 3, *Deborah Sampson: Soldier of the Revolution*
To accompany Anthology Selection 3, *James Forten*
Comprehension Skill: Following Directions

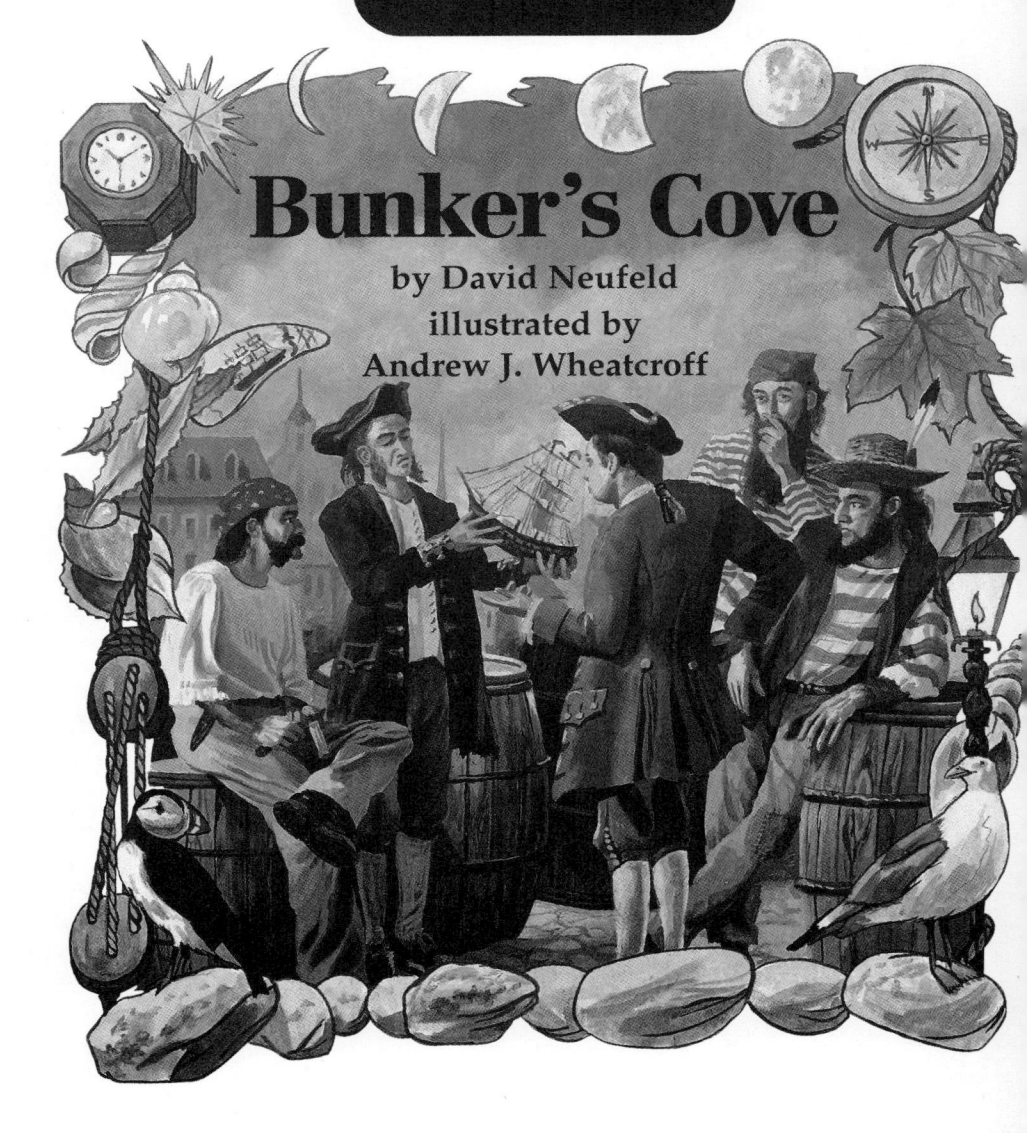

Bunker's Cove

by David Neufeld

illustrated by
Andrew J. Wheatcroff

Bunker's Cove

by David Neufeld
illustrated by
Andrew J. Wheatcroff

Strategy Focus

Jack Bunker was a sailor during the American Revolution. As you read, **evaluate** how the author presents him and his actions.

4

Responding

Think About the Selection

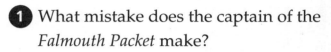

1 What mistake does the captain of the *Falmouth Packet* make?

2 How does Jack feel after he and his friend take the *Falmouth Packet* out to sea?

3 What is the author's opinion of the British sailors who chase Jack's boat?

Author's Opinions

Copy the web on a piece of paper. Complete it with words that show the author's opinion about Jack.

(?)   (Jack is plenty salty.)

What the Author Thinks About Jack

(?)   (?)

25

Jack Bunker and his friends helped the Patriots fight the British until the United States won its independence. And Jack continued to sail long after that. He lived to be a *really* old salt. That little cove where the *Falmouth Packet* lay hidden became known as Bunker's Cove. And that's its name to this day.

24

An "old salt" is a sailor who has spent years and years at sea. Back in 1773, New England was full of old salts.

Jack Bunker was one of them. He wasn't exactly old, but he was plenty salty. He'd spent so much time in boats that his feet felt unsteady on dry land.

5

Jack lived on Cranberry Island, a speck of land off the coast of Maine. His sister and her husband lived nearby. Comfort and John had a farm on Norwood's Cove, a rugged and beautiful place with mountains that rose almost straight up from the water.

Jack and his men jumped in two rowboats and rowed to the other end of the cove. There they found another opening to the sea and escaped. They rowed by night and hid during the day. They all reached home safely.

6

23

Life in Maine was pleasant and peaceful. But life was not so pleasant and peaceful elsewhere in the New England colonies. The Patriots were growing hungry for freedom from British rule.

7

No, but Jack and his friends were fast and clever. While the British warship crawled carefully along the coast, they had sailed the *Packet* toward land. Jack grabbed an axe and chopped a hole in the bottom of the boat. It sank deep into the mud.

The crew covered the *Packet* with spruce branches. They pulled seaweed from the shore and threw it over the parts of the boat that were showing. They didn't want the British to get any part of the boat. Not a single plank.

22

Right around Jack's thirty-first birthday, Massachusetts Patriots threw their famous Boston Tea Party, dumping 342 chests of tea into Boston Harbor. The tea was from the East India Company, the only company the British allowed to import tea to the colonies. By dumping it, the colonists were telling Britain they wanted freedom to make their own choices, both in matters small (what sort of tea to drink) and large (what laws to live by).

The warship sailed around to the other side of the Spruce Islands. Still fearful of running aground on the rocky coast, the British captain launched a rowboat and went through a narrow channel toward the cove where Jack and the *Packet* lay. By the time he finally reached the cove, he found nothing. Was Jack Bunker a magician?

"Cut the masts!" Jack yelled. His crew got out their axes. The masts from the *Packet* crashed down into the trees on Great Spruce Island.

The British captain saw the masts before they fell. He began to steer toward the cove. But when he reached the narrow entrance, he decided it was too dangerous to risk. "Steer clear!" he shouted to his crew.

In those days, news traveled so slowly that people in Maine didn't hear about the Boston Tea Party until a year later. Even then, they didn't get too excited. ("Those wild city folk!" they said.) But by 1776 the American Revolution was in full force. British soldiers and ships were sent to rule the unruly Americans.

20

9

Meanwhile, on Norwood's Cove, John and Comfort's farm prospered.

Then one day the British ships and soldiers came. While John and Comfort were away from their farm, the British killed the family's cows and burned their house. They left a note that said, "Starve!" When John and Comfort returned, their once thriving farm was gone.

With the British lagging behind, Jack reached his favorite hiding place on the Maine coast. It was a little cove between Great Spruce and Little Spruce Islands. The entrance was nearly invisible. Sailing into the cove was like vanishing under a magician's cloak.

Jack slipped the boat into the cove. The British weren't close enough to see where it had disappeared.

18

19

As a heavy fog began to roll in, Jack sailed by his wits. "Keep a sharp eye on the water!" he yelled to his crew.

"Rocks dead ahead!" hollered one of the men.

Jack steered the *Packet* around them. It slipped by like a ghost.

When the fog lifted, the British were still in sight. But they didn't dare go the way Jack had gone. They crept slowly along the outside edges of the rocks.

18

11

When Jack found out about this, he got mad. Mad enough to do something crazy. He and a friend set out from Norwood's Cove in a canoe. For days and days, they paddled across bays and carried their canoe across land.

Finally, they reached the Sheepscot River in Wiscassett, Maine. There they found what they'd been looking for. A British supply boat called the *Falmouth Packet,* all sixty-plus feet of it, lay peacefully at anchor. It was full of food for British troops.

The British warship was armed with a cannon. If it got within shooting distance, Jack's boat would soon look like Swiss cheese.

Some boats are just built to be faster than other boats. Warships are faster than supply boats. Lucky for Jack, though, a fast boat isn't all that counts in a chase. The captain's skill counts even more.

12

17

A few more men, hungry for adventure, volunteered to join him when he sailed the *Packet* back out to sea.

British warships were everywhere. It wasn't long before a British sailor looked through his spyglass and saw Jack at the wheel of the *Packet*. No British captain sailed without his uniform. Jack clearly was not a British captain. The chase began.

16

Not a single British sailor was on board. They were all on shore, enjoying a nap on solid ground. So Jack and his buddy climbed aboard. They raised the sails. And off they went.

The captain of the boat opened one eye and saw his boat sailing away without him. That snapped him wide awake.

Jack and his friend gave him a wave. They laughed and sang silly sailor songs as the boat went out to sea.

13

11C

Not just anyone could laugh and sing while sailing a boat like the *Falmouth Packet*.

But after a lifetime of sailing, Jack knew just how to handle the *Packet*. That's what makes a salt a salt.

The next day, Jack sailed the *Falmouth Packet* into Norwood's Cove. A boat full of supplies was a welcome sight to his sister's family. Food had been scarce since the British raid.

Jack quickly gave out the supplies. But he didn't stick around for the feast. "The British will come looking for us," he told his sister. "We don't want to be found here."

14

15

The DRUMMER BOY

by Philemon Sturges

illustrated by Tyrone Geter

Selection 2

The DRUMMER BOY

by Philemon Sturges
illustrated by Tyrone Geter

Strategy Focus

Why do Eliza and John make friends with the enemy? As you read the story, stop now and then to **summarize** what has happened.

26

Think About the Selection

1 What are two of Eliza's jobs?

2 What causes Thomas to faint?

3 Why do you think Thomas's father sets John free?

Why It Happened

Copy this chart on a piece of paper. Read what happened—the effect. Think about why it happened. Write the cause.

Story Page	Cause	Effect
35	The British and the Patriots are at war.	The British burn Captain Potter's ships, some houses, and a church.
41	?	Eliza runs to get tea, bread, and honey.
45	?	John and Eliza row Thomas back to his ship.

47

14C

Thomas did indeed move to Bristol after the American Revolution. His children and grandchildren built some of the fastest boats the world has ever seen.

IT WAS 1776. Eliza Potter lived on Ferry Point Farm in Bristol, Rhode Island. She lived with her mother, her older brother, John, and her uncle, Captain Simon Potter. She helped tend geese, grow onions, and make sails for boats.

Later that day, John and Eliza gave Thomas a ride home in their rowboat. He was too tired to march back to the ship.

"Thank you," said Thomas to John and Eliza. "When the war is over, John, I will come back and learn shipbuilding from you."

"I'd like that," said John.

"Me too," said Eliza.

28

45

"I *am* here," said John, to his sister's surprise. "But I've been taken prisoner."

"Why have you taken my son?" John's mother asked Thomas's father.

"It was King George's order," he answered.

"Well, I'm sure King George would be pleased that we have taken care of *your* son," said Eliza hopefully. "I know he would want to reward us by setting my brother free."

"I'm not sure about King George, but I will release your brother," said Thomas's father.

44

Eliza liked her chores. But most of all, she liked to sit on Seal Rock. She loved to watch ospreys dive into the sparkling water. She often saw a boy sailing a model boat on the opposite shore, and they waved to each other.

A few times each year, Eliza and John loaded a boat with onions. Then they rowed down to Newport Harbor to sell them. "Everyone loves our Bristol onions," said John. "That's mighty good for us!"

Newport had one of the very best harbors in the Colonies. It was filled with tall ships. John loved the tall ships. He was a good carpenter, and he often helped to repair them.

29

Thomas Strand lived just across the water from Eliza and John. His father was the commander of the British soldiers in Newport. Thomas was the drummer boy in his father's regiment.

Thomas liked living in the British army camp. And he enjoyed marching to the beat of his own drum. But most of all he liked making model boats. Back home in England, his model boats had won prizes. Thomas still sailed one of his boats when he had free time. It usually caught a brisk southwest wind and sped toward Seal Rock on the opposite shore. Sometimes he saw a girl sitting on Seal Rock, and they waved to each other.

30

43

Thomas's father bent down to see what had happened to his son.

When Thomas opened his eyes, he saw his father and then Eliza. They recognized each other from all the times they had waved across the water.

First Thomas ate a bit and had a sip of tea. Then he said to Eliza, "Thank you. I hope no one has been hurt. I meant no harm to anyone. If fact, when the war stops, I want to stay in Bristol and work on boats."

"I wish my brother was here to talk to you," said Eliza. "He's a skilled carpenter and he works on boats."

42

31

When the soldiers and their prisoners got to Ferry Point Farm, Eliza and her mother were standing next to the barn. The soldiers were so tired that they decided to rest there for a while. The commander told Eliza and her mother to bring water for the soldiers. At first Eliza and her mother didn't want to help the soldiers in any way. But then a young Lobsterback boy fainted right in front of them. Eliza ran to get him some tea and some bread with honey.

32

41

For Thomas, the march back to the British ship seemed much longer than the march toward the Potter boatyard. He had long since passed from hungry and tired to thirsty, hot, and exhausted. No one seemed to notice that his drumming had stopped and he was falling behind.

John was more angry and frightened than tired. He felt a bit better when he realized that the soldiers were headed in the direction of his home, Ferry Point Farm.

40

Thomas and his father often rowed over to Bristol to have a look around. Thomas hoped to meet the girl who waved, but he never did.

Like Newport Harbor, Bristol Harbor was full of tall ships. "The ones over there belong to Captain Simon Potter, the Patriot leader," said Thomas's father. "I'm sure that he and his men are planning something. They say you can't trust those Patriots."

"Is that why we're here in the Colonies, because we can't trust the Patriots?" Thomas asked.

"In a way," said his father. "We're keeping order in the Colonies, and we have our hands full. The Patriots don't like being told what to do by King George. I won't be surprised if soon there is a war between Britain and the Patriots."

33

34

39

At the Potter boatyard, all of the carpenters were busy. Eliza and her mother had gone home to make lunch for the hungry crew.

Suddenly someone cried out, "The Lobsterbacks are coming!" But it was too late. When John looked over the side of the unfinished boat, he saw British soldiers coming his way. They were led by a drummer boy about his own age.

The soldiers captured John and his shipbuilding friends. They set the ship and the boatyard on fire. Then they began marching their prisoners back toward the British ship north of Bristol Harbor.

Thomas's father was right. In July 1776, the British and the Patriots went to war. In August, British ships sneaked into Bristol Harbor. They burned down Captain Potter's ships, a church, and several houses.

But the Patriots had spirit and energy. They were not discouraged. Soon Captain Potter began to build a new ship. John and Eliza had to help their uncle. John did some of the carpentry. Eliza and her mother sewed the sails. It was very hard work. When they complained a bit to their mother, she said, "It's for the cause of liberty."

Meanwhile, back in Newport at the British army camp, Thomas's father was getting ready to march. He said to Thomas, "King George has ordered us to destroy any ships that Captain Potter is building. And our spies tell us that he is building one near Bristol Harbor. We've got to hurry!"

Thomas put on his bright red uniform. His drum rolled smartly as he and his father led the soldiers to Newport Harbor. There they boarded a twenty-gun ship and sailed off toward Bristol.

The soldiers landed just north of Bristol Harbor. With Thomas in front, the soldiers marched toward the boatyard in which Captain Potter's ship was being built. As he drummed, Thomas admired the bright red coats all around him.

Now I know why the Patriots call us Lobsterbacks, he thought. Thinking about lobsters made Thomas hungry. He was tired too. It was a long, long march.

36

37

Deborah Sampson
Soldier of the Revolution

by Lee S. Justice
illustrated by Ron Himler

Deborah Sampson
Soldier of the Revolution

by Lee S. Justice
illustrated by Ron Himler

Strategy Focus

Is freedom for everyone? As you read this story, think of other **questions** for discussion.

48

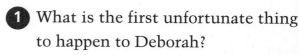

Responding

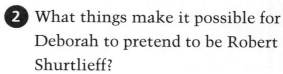

Think About the Story

1. What is the first unfortunate thing to happen to Deborah?

2. What things make it possible for Deborah to pretend to be Robert Shurtlieff?

3. Pretend you are Mrs. Thomas. Make a numbered list of directions for Deborah Sampson to follow when she completes her jobs on the farm. Begin with **1. Get up at dawn.**

Following Directions

Help Deborah Sampson plan her speech. Write these directions in the right order on a piece of paper. Circle the clue words.

Third, tell about the hardships of army life.
Next, tell about being a bound girl.
Finally, tell about how you were wounded.
First, begin with your early life.

69

Audiences paid to see the unusual soldier. In uniform, Deborah Sampson Gannett performed the drills she had learned as Private Shurtlieff.

She gave her speech in a confident voice. Pretending to be a man was a "bad deed," she admitted. She had taken steps that women were not permitted to take. Terrible memories of the "storms of war" would always be with her. Yet she had done it for the best reasons — liberty and independence.

The new United States government granted small monthly payments to those who had served in the war. Deborah Sampson Gannett was granted payments for her faithful service as a soldier of the Revolution.

Deborah Sampson was born in Plympton, Massachusetts, in 1760. Throughout her childhood, she heard about Boston's Patriots, also called the Sons of Liberty. She heard the talk of independence — of breaking free of Britain.

68

49

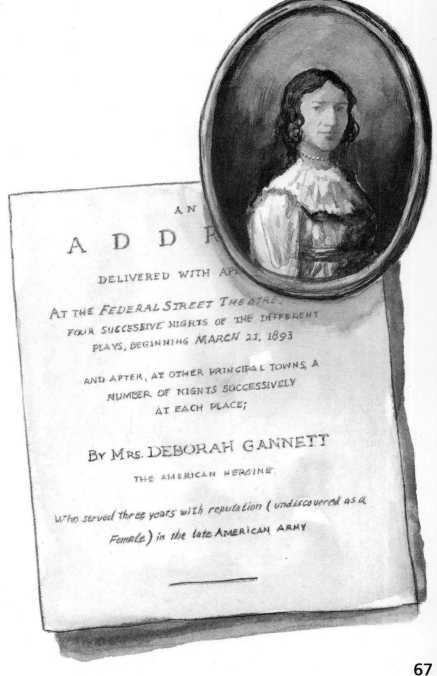

AN

ADDR

DELIVERED WITH APP

AT THE FEDERAL STREET THEATRE,
FOUR SUCCESSIVE NIGHTS OF THE DIFFERENT
PLAYS, BEGINNING MARCH 21, 1893

AND AFTER, AT OTHER PRINCIPAL TOWNS, A
NUMBER OF NIGHTS SUCCESSIVELY
AT EACH PLACE;

BY MRS. DEBORAH GANNETT
THE AMERICAN HEROINE,

Who served three years with reputation (undiscovered as a
Female) in the late AMERICAN ARMY.

50

67

28C

Deborah Sampson married a farmer named Benjamin Gannett. The couple had three children. They struggled to make a living on their farm.

Years later, Deborah Gannett met a newspaper publisher. He wrote a book based on her life.

The Gannetts worked hard. But they still owed money. In 1802, the newspaper publisher came to Deborah with another idea. How would she like to make money by telling her story to audiences?

In 1802, women did not go on speaking tours. It just was not done. Deborah Sampson Gannett, forty-two years old, thought about the newspaperman's offer. She would have to travel from city to city on her own. She would have to perform before strangers. She would have to memorize a fifteen-page speech.

Deborah said yes. She would do it.

Freedom was a dangerous and exciting idea. But there was little freedom in Deborah's own life. As she later said, "I was born to be unfortunate."

When she was very young, Deborah's father sailed off on a ship and never came back. Her mother did not have enough money for food. So she decided to look for a family to take her daughter.

Often, poor parents "bound out" a child to another family. In return for a home, food, and clothing, the child would serve the family until age eighteen. Ten-year-old Deborah became a bound servant in the home of the Thomas family of Middleborough.

52

65

30C

Then came a morning when Deborah was not so lucky. In a battle with Tories, she was wounded in the head and leg. She begged her comrades not to take her to the hospital. "Let me die here," she pleaded. But they did not listen.

A French doctor at a field hospital treated Deborah's head. She said she had no other wound. The doctor noticed the bloody boot. "Sit you down, my lad," said the doctor, preparing to look at the leg. But Deborah said there was no need.

She secretly tried to remove the musket ball from her own thigh, with no success. The wound would heal, but not fully.

In 1783, Deborah was among the troops in Philadelphia. Sickness spread throughout the city. She became ill. She was brought to a hospital. Her fever was so high that she passed out. When a doctor looked her over, he discovered that the soldier called Robert Shurtlieff was really a girl.

Soon afterward, Deborah Sampson received an honorable discharge from the Continental Army. She returned to Massachusetts.

The Thomases treated Deborah like a daughter. Of course, sons and daughters were expected to work. Mrs. Thomas told Deborah what she should do each day.

First, Deborah had to get up at dawn to begin her household chores. Then, she must help make breakfast for the family. Next, she should feed the chickens and milk the cow. Then, she should water the vegetable garden. After that, she could sew, spin, or weave. Like all farm women, Deborah worked hard.

With the ten Thomas sons, Deborah also hunted and fished. She chopped wood and gathered hay. She did all kinds of heavy work.

64

53

It was 1782. Fifty recruits hiked west through the Berkshire hills. Hour after hour, they kept moving without a rest. Deborah, marching among the men, suddenly realized what she had done. She felt terror. If the army found out she was a woman, she surely would be punished. She might be hanged!

Deborah calmed herself. In the days and months ahead, she would have to be watchful. She would play the part of a quiet young man who kept to himself.

After ten tiring days, the recruits reached West Point in New York. There, they received uniforms and weapons. Deborah began training as a foot soldier in the Fourth Massachusetts Regiment.

The war was winding down. But British troops and Tory bands were still active in New York. Deborah joined scouting parties hunting for armed Tories. She faced musket fire. She heard the cries of the wounded. She saw men fall beside her. Luckily, she escaped unharmed.

54

63

Farmer Thomas didn't believe in schooling for girls. But Deborah had always been eager to learn. She already knew how to read and write.

Deborah read all the pamphlets and newspapers she could find. A minister gave her a religious book. She soon knew it by heart. She kept a journal. In it, she listed her good actions and her bad ones. She wanted to improve herself.

"I wish you wouldn't spend so much time scribbling," Farmer Thomas complained. But he did not make her stop. So Deborah continued.

At church one day, someone read an important document to the crowd. The document said, "All men are created equal." It said that people had rights — "life, liberty, and the pursuit of happiness." It listed the reasons for breaking free of Britain. At the end of the reading, the listeners leaped up and cheered.

The Declaration of Independence made Deborah's heart pound. But she wondered what some of it meant. She wondered about words like *liberty*.

The soldiers were fighting for liberty. The older Thomas boys had already left home and signed up. Was liberty only for a nation? Or could there be liberty for a sixteen-year-old farm girl?

56

61

One day Deborah's Middleborough neighbors saw her going about her business as usual. The next morning she was gone.

Days later, a young man in farmer's clothes stood before an army recruiter in Bellingham, Massachusetts. "Your age?" asked the recruiter.

"Eighteen," said the young man. His face did not even have a whisker. He looked fifteen, even younger. But the army needed soldiers — young or old. The recruiter did not care.

The young farmer promised to serve for a term of three years. He signed his name: *Robert Shurtlieff.*

Robert Shurtlieff was not a teenage boy. He was Deborah Sampson in disguise.

60

57

35C

When she turned eighteen, Deborah began working in people's homes as a weaver. She also taught children for two summers. But by the time she was twenty-one, she was eager for a change.

Deborah had an active mind. She was quiet, but in a strong, confident way. Deborah looked strong, too. And she had grown taller than other women of the time. In fact, she was taller than many men.

But while men her age had a chance to see the world and taste freedom, women didn't. Deborah decided she wanted adventure, too.

58

59

HOUGHTON MIFFLIN
Reading
A Legacy of Literacy

Person to Person

THEME 4

Person to Person

Reader's Library Selection 1, *Something for Everyone*
To accompany Anthology Selection 1, *Mariah Keeps Cool*
Comprehension Skill: Problem Solving/Decision Making

Reader's Library Selection 2, *Pretty Cool, for a Cat*
To accompany Anthology Selection 2, *Mom's Best Friend*
Comprehension Skill: Noting Details

Reader's Library Selection 3, *Trevor from Trinidad*
To accompany Anthology Selection 3, *Yang the Second and Her Secret Admirers*
Comprehension Skill: Compare/Contrast

Reader's Library Selection 4, *Upstate Autumn*
To accompany Anthology Selection 4, *Dear Mr. Henshaw*
Comprehension Skill: Making Inferences

Something for Everyone

by Joanne Korba

illustrated by Nancy Carpenter

Something for Everyone

by Joanne Korba
illustrated by Nancy Carpenter

Strategy Focus

Tony, Jay, and Elvis choose music for a neighborhood party. As you read, **predict** what their choices will be and **infer** how the party will turn out.

4

Responding

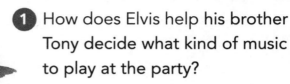

Think About the Selection

1 How does Elvis help his brother Tony decide what kind of music to play at the party?

2 Why do Tony and Jay decide to play many different kinds of music?

3 Making a big party can be a problem for one person. What does Tony's mom do about that?

Find Solutions

Copy the chart on a piece of paper. Read Tony and Jay's problem. Write solutions you read about in the story. Then circle the one you think is the best.

Problem	Solutions
Tony and Jay have to decide what music to tape for the party.	1. Tape music people can really dance to. 2. ? 3. ?

25

Even Mr. Bromley.

Everyone who lives in the Santiagos' neighborhood calls it the UN — the United Nations. That's because the neighbors come in all colors and nationalities. English is spoken here. But so are Chinese, Portuguese, Russian, Haitian Creole, Laotian, and more than one kind of Spanish.

Every summer, the UN has a big neighborhood party. There's always lots of food, fun, and friendship. Neighbors take turns being in charge. Last summer it was the Santiagos' turn.

24

5

"Then we're agreed," Mrs. Santiago was saying over the phone. "We'll have the party at the end of July. It's going to be great this year! We'll talk more later, *amiga*."

As she hung up, her son Tony walked into the kitchen. He was followed by his best friend, Jay. "You're looking at one-half of this year's UN Party Committee," Mrs. Santiago announced proudly. "I just asked your mother to be the other half," she said to Jay. "These parties are getting too big for one family to manage."

That year, the UN party was hot in every way. The Fourth of July sun was hot. Hamburgers, turkey burgers, fish, steaks, chicken, and ribs sizzled hot and smoky on the grill. And most of all, there was the dance music. It was hot, hot, hot!

Because there was something for everyone on the dance tape, everyone danced. Every man, woman, and child in the UN. *Everybody.*

6

23

4D

"So you admit it," Mrs. Santiago said when the tapes were finished. "Your little brother was a big help to you."

"Let's not get carried away, Mami," said Tony. "He started off by being a big *pain*." His mother put her hands on her hips. "Okay, okay!" Tony said. "In the end, he was kind of a help. Maybe a pretty big help. All right, all right. We couldn't have done it without him!" He sighed.

His mother patted his cheek. "You're a good big brother," she said.

22

Tony Santiago and Jay Kovak had been best friends since they were in preschool. Now they were 11 years old and in the same sixth-grade class. They were on the same Little League team, and they played for the same after-school hockey team. They liked the same computer games and read the same books.

Their parents were friends too. It made sense for the Santiagos and Kovaks to work together on the neighborhood party.

7

"What about Papi?" Tony asked his mother. "Isn't he doing anything for the party?"

"We put him in charge of the barbecues," his mother answered. "Along with Jay's dad."

"Hey, a Santiago and a Kovak should be in charge of music, too!" said Tony, pointing to himself and Jay. "*We* know what's hot and what's not."

8

With the help of Elvis and two of his friends, they carried out the plan quickly. House by house, they gathered armloads of music. There were 50-year-old records, 25-year-old tapes, and brand-new CDs. They had enough music to make dance tapes for five years' worth of parties!

21

    6D

Tony's plan was to ask every person in the neighborhood — every man, woman, and child (except really little kids) — to give him a recording of their favorite dance tune. Then he and Jay could put all the tunes on tape.

20

"M-m-m-m," his mother answered. She looked doubtful. But after a few silent moments, she said, "Okay. But just remember — the music is meant to entertain people. To make them sing and dance and enjoy themselves. That's the point."

Jay nodded. "Sure, sure, Mrs. Santiago," he said. "We can do that." He turned to Tony. "Come on! Let's go to my house and figure out what music we want to use."

The boys headed for the door. "Tony!" Mrs. Santiago called out sweetly. "Haven't you forgotten something?"

9

7D

Mr. Bromley spent most of his time on his front porch, frowning at everyone who passed by. He usually greeted Jay and Tony with "You kids stay off my grass!"

"Mr. Bromley!" said Elvis. "He won't dance no matter what we play! You *can't* think of something for every single person in the neighborhood."

"I guess maybe that's true," Jay said.

"No, it's not!" Tony shot back. He was smiling. "I have a plan."

10

19

8D

"But . . ." Tony began. Two heads swiveled toward him. Tony didn't agree? How could Tony have a problem? He was always the peacemaker.

"How do *we* know what kind of dance music everyone likes?" Tony asked. "Maybe there's Chinese dance music that we don't know about. And Brazilian music. Then there's Mr. Bromley. What kind of music do you suppose *he* likes?"

Tony stopped and sighed. He'd almost managed to escape.

"Come on, Tony. You know you're supposed to look after your brother in the afternoon. I have to work in peace." Mrs. Santiago wrote an advice column for a local paper. "We agreed!" she said.

"Yeah. I know, Mami," Tony answered. He sighed again as he walked into the hall. "Elvis!" he called. "Come on down! We're going over to Jay's."

Then he leaned against the wall, waiting. And waiting. And waiting.

His brother took his time coming downstairs. He didn't like the afternoon babysitting arrangement any better than his brother did. "I just happen to be reading a really good book," Elvis complained. "Why do I have to stop and go to Jay's?"

"Because we're in charge of the dance music for the neighborhood party," Tony said. "Jay and I have to decide what to tape. But hey, bring your book. You can read while we have our meeting."

18

11

9D

Elvis's eyes lit up. "*We're* in charge of the dance music? Cool! I know all about dance music. I'm a great dancer. You two can just leave it all to me!" He ran out the door, heading for Jay's house.

"No, no, you've got it wrong. It's just Jay and me! Hey . . . wait!" Tony called, dashing down the sidewalk after Elvis.

Jay followed the pair, shaking his head. He was pretty sure that the first meeting of the UN Dance Music Committee wasn't going to go well.

"There's something else we have to remember," Elvis told Tony and Jay. "We can't just have dance music that kids like. We need to make sure that we have music our parents like. And older people too!"

Jay caught on. "Right! We need some disco and funk. Mambos. Cha-chas. And swing music, for that kind of dance they did in the old days. . . . "

"You mean the jitterbug?" Elvis asked.

"Yeah!" cried Jay. "Now we'll really have something for everyone."

12

17

"Rap and hip-hop are the same thing," Elvis mumbled.

"No, they're not," Tony said firmly, although he wasn't sure. "Anyway, the point is that for the United Nations party, we need United Nations music."

"That's true," Jay said, nodding. "Music from other countries."

"Latin music is from other countries," Elvis mumbled. He frowned down at the floor, thinking. Suddenly, he looked up.

They all sat on the floor of the sunporch that Jay used as a bedroom. Tony looked through his friend's CDs. Jay had a notepad in his lap. "We should make a list of the music we want to tape," he said to Tony. He was trying to ignore Elvis. "How many tapes should we make?"

Before Tony could answer, Elvis started talking. "We have to tape music that people can really dance to. That means Latin music. Everyone knows it has the best dance beat." He got up and started dancing to an imaginary song.

16

13

"Don't you have a book to read?" was all Tony said to Elvis.

But Jay was ready to argue. "Well, *this* everyone doesn't agree. If we're talking about great dance music, I have some techno albums that are perfect!"

"Okay, that's set. Latin music and techno music," Tony said soothingly. "Great. I think this meeting is going really well. . . ."

"Techno? You mean that computer junk?" Elvis sniffed. "That's not real music!"

"Excuse me?" Jay said coldly.

Jay and Elvis glared at each other. Tony got between them. "Hey, hey," he said. "Why make this an argument between two kinds of music? Why can't we have both? In fact, we should have all different kinds of music — rock, country, rap, hip-hop. . . ."

14

15

PRETTY COOL, FOR A CAT

by Kitty Colton

illustrated by Amanda Harvey

PRETTY COOL, FOR A CAT

by Kitty Colton
illustrated by Amanda Harvey

Strategy Focus

Toby is an amusing pet. As you read, **monitor** and **clarify** your understanding of how animals can help people feel better.

26

Responding

THINK ABOUT THE SELECTION

1. Do you think Peter's parents are right to give him a cat instead of the dog he wanted?

2. How does Toby make Peter and his parents laugh?

3. How does Peter help make Matt feel better?

NOTING DETAILS

Copy the web on a piece of paper and write details in the ovals that support the main idea in the box.

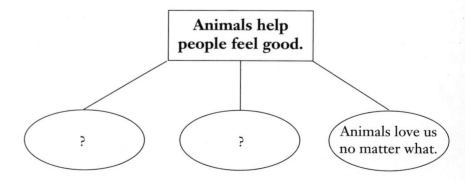

Animals help people feel good.

?

?

Animals love us no matter what.

47

On our way out, we saw Maria. She told us about a special program that trains people and animals to work with patients, one on one.

"Different people need different kinds of attention," she explained. "Some like animals who clown around and make them laugh."

"Toby can do that," I said.

"Others want an animal to pet and cuddle," she said, "so they feel less lonely."

"Toby can do that," I said.

And she did.

I'd been wanting a dog since — well, since I could say the word *dog*. According to Mom, I learned to say "dog" even before I said "Mom" or "Dad."

I never got one, though. My parents said, "Too much work." Still, every year, especially around my birthday, I begged them.

46

27

When I was really little, I got stuffed dogs. A lot of them. My bedroom was like a kennel without the barks. Then my parents tried to interest me in other pets. First it was a mouse, then a turtle, then a goldfish. All very nice and very easy to take care of, according to my parents. And all very, very boring.

The October before my ninth birthday, I started up the same old whine. "Ple-e-e-a-s-e can I get a dog this year?" I begged. "I will totally take care of him. You won't even know he's here."

When we finally left, Matt made us promise to bring Toby on every visit. "She's pretty cool — for a cat," he said, giving her one last belly rub.

28

45

16D

I decided to give Matt some time to change his mind. So I went downstairs to get some magazines. When I came back, Matt was nowhere in sight. Neither was Toby.

"Hey, we're down here, man!" Matt shouted. He was speeding down the hall in his wheelchair, Toby on his shoulder. Several other kids were following behind. "This cat isn't so bad after all," he said. "She's cracking everyone up."

I followed Matt as he wheeled into the lounge. Other kids gathered around to pat her as she draped herself on Matt's arm. She lapped up all that attention like a bowl of cream. I could tell Matt liked the attention too.

Mom snorted. "Peter, you can't even take care of your socks," she said. I could tell she wasn't softening.

"But Matt has a dog. Matt doesn't take care of his socks," I said. Matt was my best friend.

"That dog is a prime example of why we are not getting a dog," Mom said.

I thought she was being unfair. True, Pluto was a bit of a pest. He ate the Simpsons' furniture. And he bit people. But he was still a good dog, basically. Matt boasted about him all the time, and brought him everywhere. Sometimes I got a little jealous.

44

29

17D

On my birthday, my dad came home carrying a box poked with holes. It was way too small for a puppy — or was it? Maybe he'd got me a puppy that was born just two days ago? "Dad!" I shouted.

Then I heard a soft small noise coming from inside. It was no kind of a bark. It sounded more like — a meow?

Dad reached into the box and lifted out a tiny orange furball. "She's all yours," he said with a grin. "Happy birthday!"

The furball quivered in my hands. I tried to hide my disappointment. A cat? When did I ever say anything about a cat?

I had picked out a dog name years ago. Toby — as in October, my birthday month. The furball had to be called something.

A couple of days later, Dad and I took a very clean Toby to the care center to visit Matt. I hoped no chickens would be visiting that day.

When we got to Matt's doorway, I put Toby on the floor so she could get used to the place. But before I could say more than "Hi" to Matt, Toby had jumped onto his bed.

"What in the — " Matt started. "Your *cat*?"

"Yeah. Toby," I reminded him. "I thought it might be fun to have her around for a while."

"I don't even *like* cats," Matt said, as Toby nuzzled his neck.

30

43

Maria handed me a sheet of paper. "Here are some rules to read before you bring Toby in for a visit. For one thing, she'll have to take a bath before she comes in."

Dad and I looked at each other and rolled our eyes.

"It's a rule," she said with a shrug. "No bath, no visit. She'll have to get a checkup too. Plus, Toby needs to behave herself when she's here. Just like you do."

I was starting to worry. Toby was a great cat, but she wasn't so good with rules, except the kind she made and we followed.

Mom and Dad liked Toby because she didn't need to be walked, and she didn't eat furniture the way Pluto did. But they liked her for other reasons too, reasons that weren't practical. I could tell. So did I, despite myself.

Toby was no dog, that's for sure. But for a cat she was pretty cool. She made us crack up about a hundred times a day. There was the way she stalked around the house like a tiger, for one thing. Or how she'd fall off the table, then act as if she'd done it on purpose. Or how she'd try to catch a fly in midair, miss, and then pretend she was just stretching.

42

31

It wasn't just the clowny stuff, though. Toby was a pal, even though she wouldn't walk me to school, the way Matt's dog did. She wouldn't fetch a stick either, or bound over and knock me down so she could lick my face.

"What *does* she do?" Matt asked. "Cats are good for nothing, if you ask me." I never asked him.

"Don't blame yourself," Maria told me. "Sometimes patients feel helpless. Or they think you're bored with them. Or they're a little mad at you because you are well and they aren't. Or they're just scared.

"That's one of the reasons animals are so helpful. Animals don't care how we look or how we act. They love us no matter what. And that means they can make people feel better even when friends and families can't."

I thought about all the times Toby had done that for me.

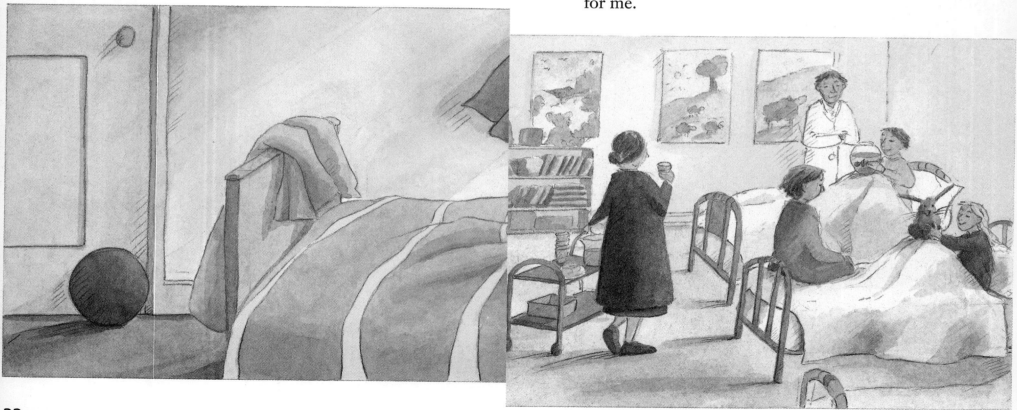

32

41

"You can see it happening," Maria continued. "When patients pet the animals, their whole mood changes. And animals don't just make people *feel* better — they can really help them *get* better."

"Well, *I'm* not having any luck making Matt feel better *or* get better," I said, kicking at a speck of dirt.

Toby slept on the end of my bed every night. When winter came, she slept on my feet to keep them warm. I don't know how she knew to do that. But she did. When I didn't get picked for the baseball team, I went into my room and shut the door and fell on my bed and cried. Then Toby started rubbing against my face, and her tail tickled me. I couldn't help laughing.

She always did stuff like that. I couldn't explain that stuff to Matt. I don't know why.

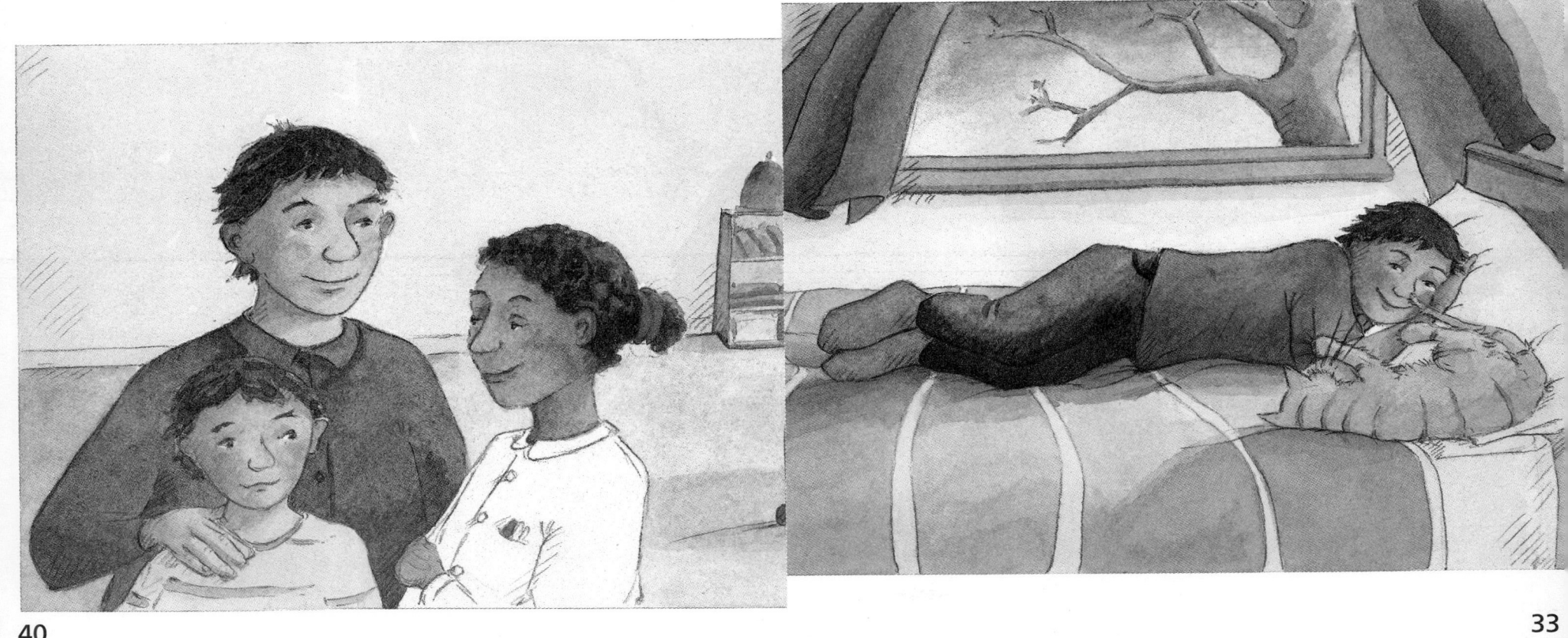

40

33

Over the next year, we watched Toby grow from a kitten into a cat. After a while, it was impossible to imagine life without her. When my next birthday came around, I didn't even ask for a dog. Toby wouldn't like it. And it was her house now.

A little while after I turned ten, Matt got in a bad accident. He was riding his bike and got hit by a car. One of his legs and his hip got all messed up. He was in the hospital for a long time, and for a while I couldn't even see him. Then he got moved to another place, called a care center. They were supposed to help him learn to walk again.

Matt seemed so different when I went to see him. I couldn't figure out if he was sad, or mad, or both. He told me he hated being in bed all the time. I think he was scared about his leg, too, and whether he'd ever be able to play soccer, or even walk. But he wouldn't say so, even to me, his best friend.

"How can chickens make people feel better?" I asked.

"You boil them up and make them into soup," Dad said.

Maria frowned at him. "Scientists have found that animals can make sick people get well faster," she said, looking at me. "Cats, dogs, even *chickens* — almost any animal that's comfortable around people. They all seem to help people who are healing, or dealing with a handicap, or going through a tough time. Just petting an animal can make people feel less worried and less lonely." I knew that was true.

34

39

We asked Maria, the nurse who took care of Matt. She smiled when we said we'd like to bring Toby to visit. "I think Matt would love that," she said. "He's always going on about that dog of his. But Pluto sounds a little too — umm — excitable for this place."

"Animals are okay, though?" Dad asked.

"Sure!" she replied. "We love having animal visitors. We've had all sorts over the past couple of years. Dogs, cats, rabbits too. Once we had a goat. Some other places have had llamas, horses, even chickens!"

38

35

23D

I think he missed school, too, but he wouldn't say that either. He did keep saying how much he missed Pluto, though.

That's when I first got the idea. "Why don't we bring Pluto in to visit Matt?" I asked my dad when he came to pick me up.

Dad laughed and said, "Are you nuts? Those kids in there are hurting already. The last thing they need is to get their arms bitten off." I guess he had a point.

"What about Toby, then?" I asked. "She loves people. I bet Toby could cheer Matt up."

Dad was quiet for a minute. Then we both burst out laughing, just thinking about it. "Let's find out if animals are allowed," Dad said.

36

37

24D

Trevor from Trinidad

by Delores Lowe Friedman
illustrated by Ann Boyajian

Selection 3

Trevor from Trinidad

by Delores Lowe Friedman
illustrated by Ann Boyajian

Strategy Focus

Trevor is starting school in a new country. As you read, ask **questions** about how Trevor is getting used to the change.

48

Responding

Think About the Selection

1. Why does Trevor have trouble when he moves to the United States?

2. Why does Trevor's teacher have the class do research on their backgrounds?

3. Compare Trevor's school in Trinidad and his new one.

Compare and Contrast

Copy the chart. Read the description. Put a check where the description fits.

Description	Trevor	Friends at School
calls the teacher "mum"		
wears jeans to school		
calls soccer "football"		
likes to be in the school play		
shares things about other cultures		

69

When they got to the front door, Trevor said, "Samantha, did you call me Trevi?"

"I just heard Veronica call you that," said Sam with a smile. "I think she likes you."

Trevor said nothing. He might as well just accept his clever "pain" of a little sister. There had been nobody quite like her in Trinidad.

68

Until he was ten years old, Trevor lived in Trinidad, an island in the West Indies. Trevor's mother died when he was four. That same year, his father left Trinidad to find work in America, and Trevor went to live with his grandmother. His father called long distance, and Trevor sent him lots of letters. At first, his grandmother wrote the words, and Trevor drew pictures and signed his name. In every letter, Trevor said he couldn't wait until he could go live in the United States with his father.

49

Finally, Trevor got the call he was waiting for. It was time to move to the United States! His father had a good job, he had married again, and Trevor had a new stepsister named Samantha.

On his first day of school in his new country, Trevor wore blue jeans. Samantha had insisted on them. She said she would not walk with him to school unless he dressed "normally." In Trinidad, everyone looked the same in their school uniforms. There, he didn't have to worry about standing out.

"Samantha, are you sure these clothes are all right?" Trevor asked. He spoke with the accent of his homeland.

"I told you to call me Sam!" she replied. "Next time you call me Samantha, I won't answer."

"But . . ." Trevor started.

"You look fine!" she said. "It's too bad you don't *sound* normal."

"What's not normal?" Trevor asked.

"Oh, never mind," Sam said, sucking her teeth. "That's your class over there. Oh, poor you! Veronica Bowen and Tameka Wilson are in your class."

On the way home from school, Sam asked, "How'd it go today?"

"Great! They asked me to design the scenery in the class play," said Trevor.

"I figured they would, Trevi," Sam said.

50

67

28D

Everyone listened closely to Trevor's report. Their eyes lit up as he showed them his drawings. When he finished, the children applauded.

Veronica raised her hand and told Ms. Ruskin,

"Trevor should do the scenery for our play." Juan and Tameka nodded in agreement. Ms. Ruskin smiled.

"Trevor, would you like to be our scenic designer?" she asked.

"Yes!" Trevor answered excitedly.

Trevor hadn't expected Sam to come up with such a good idea. She usually spent her time making fun of him. But Carnival was the perfect topic! When he described it to his class, they would see how wonderful Trinidad is and all the reasons he missed living there.

Over the weekend, Trevor wrote his report. He made colorful paintings of costumes. He sketched the steel drums the musicians played. Then he chose one of his father's records to play. He called his report "Carnival in Trinidad."

52

65

30D

"Trevor, why aren't you eating?" asked his father. "Joyce made this meal especially for you. She called Granny to get the recipes."

"I'm sorry," Trevor said, and then he blurted everything on his mind. "I was just thinking about Trinidad. I have to do a report on it for school, and I don't know what to say. I mean, there's so *much* to say! How can I focus on one thing? Veronica did hers on Jamaica, and she brought in tropical fruits. But I don't want to talk about food, or games, or stuff like that. I want to think of something that will really show what the people of Trinidad are like. Then maybe everyone will understand *me* better, too."

"Why don't you do a report on Carnival?" offered Sam. "You can use your drawings and paintings to show what the costumes look like."

"And we have some great Carnival music," Trevor's dad added.

Trevor stood behind the last boy in line. He pushed his glasses up on the bridge of his nose. He tried as hard as he could to blend into the background. The teacher had gray hair and a round, warm face. She looked at him kindly, and then she looked down at a piece of paper in her hand. "And your name is . . . ?" She looked up at him again.

"My name is Trevor Rainford, mum," he answered.

"Did he say MUM?" whispered a girl to his right.

"You must be the young man from Trinidad," said the teacher. "Nice to meet you, Trevor. I am Ms. Ruskin."

Trevor felt all eyes on him. The children whispered and pointed. His hopes of blending in were dashed.

Ms. Ruskin wrote her name on the board, and then she showed Trevor his seat. She asked all the children to introduce themselves to him. One by one, they called out their names. Trevor couldn't remember any of them. Then Ms. Ruskin asked, "Why don't you come up and tell everyone a little about yourself, Trevor?"

64

53

Trevor walked slowly to the front of the class. He remembered his teacher in Trinidad scolding him about speaking too softly and not standing straight. So he stood up as straight as he could, and in a strong voice he said, "My name is Trevor Rainford. I come from Trinidad. That's an island in the West Indies. It is close to the equator, so it is very hot. I like to read, draw, and paint . . . ."

Tameka giggled. "He talks funny," she whispered loudly to Veronica.

"He's got an accent," said Veronica.

Trevor heard them. "Where *I* come from," he said, "*you* are the ones who have an accent."

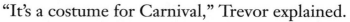

That night, Sam started setting the dinner table while Trevor doodled. Sam looked at his drawing. "Whatever that is, would you please move it so I can set the table?" she asked.

"It's a costume for Carnival," Trevor explained.

"It's very nice. Now move it," Sam said.

Trevor's stepmother, Joyce, laid a platter of curried chicken on the dinner table. It looked delicious. But Trevor had no appetite.

54

63

After the reports for that day, Ms. Ruskin had an idea. "What if we turn everything we're learning into a play?" she asked the class. "We'd have to write a script, and make costumes and scenery."

"Yes!" the class shouted. Trevor's eyes sparkled with excitement.

"We'll wait until all the reports are done. Then we can begin to work on the show," said Ms. Ruskin. "Those of you who have not given your report should bring it in on Monday."

"Trevor has a good point," Ms. Ruskin said. "Now I'd like all of you to make Trevor feel welcome. Russell and Juan, I'd like you to show him around today."

The two boys looked over to Trevor and waved. At noon, they ate lunch together, and then Juan asked Trevor if he wanted to play ball. Trevor nodded his head happily. "I play football," he told them.

62

55

33D

"In the spring we play baseball, not football," Juan said.

"Oh come on, let's play football with him today," Russell said cheerfully. The three ran outside. The equipment teacher helped Russell dig out a football. Russell threw it to Trevor. Trevor just stared at the oddly shaped ball as it hit him in the chest.

"That's not a football," he said as the ball hit the ground. He watched it bounce this way and that.

The next day in class, some children gave reports on the countries their families came from. Miko shared stories about Japan. Then it was Veronica's turn. Like Trevor, she had roots in the West Indies. Her grandfather was from Jamaica. She brought in tropical fruits for the class to taste. "These are mangoes, and this is a coconut," she said. "And this is . . ." She looked blank.

"A papaya!" Trevor offered. Veronica smiled at him and continued her report. He drew a mango tree and a papaya tree in his notebook.

56

61

34D

When they got back to the classroom, the boys told Ms. Ruskin what had happened. She smiled and said, "Of course. In Trinidad the game we call *soccer* is known as *football*."

Ms. Ruskin looked thoughtful for a moment. Then she told the class, "I have an idea. I'd like every one of you to do some research. Find out about where your family lived before they came to the United States. Ask your parents and grandparents, or anybody who can help. Try to learn about foods, games, songs, and dances — anything that made that place special. Next week, you can tell the class what you have learned."

60

57

35D

A few days later, Sam and Trevor were doing their homework when Sam blurted out, "Veronica Bowen says you are stuck up."

Trevor began to doodle on the blank sheet of paper next to his math homework. Ms. Ruskin had said he was a good math student. He just needed to learn how they did long division in America.

"I don't think much of Veronica," he replied. "And I don't care what she says. She spends more time talking and giggling than she does studying. In Trinidad, Ms. Crown would . . . ."

"Trinidad, Trinidad! That's all you think about," Sam said.

"I like thinking about Trinidad," Trevor answered quietly. "I miss the beach, and I miss my friends."

"If you were in Trinidad right now, what would you be doing?" asked Sam, her voice suddenly kinder.

"Right about now, Granny would be making costumes for Carnival," he remembered out loud. While his grandmother sewed, he used to sit on the porch, doing sketches. The walls of his house were covered with his drawings and paintings. Many of the carnival dancers and musicians came in and out of the house, trying on their costumes and telling him how good his sketches were.

"Well, there's no Carnival here," Sam snapped.

Trevor didn't notice her impatience. He was caught up in happy memories of Carnival season. Carnival was part of him, and he was proud of it. He loved the music, the dancing, and the celebration. Best of all, he loved being in the middle of it all.

58

59

Upstate Autumn

by Jed Mannheimer
illustrated by Mark Elliott

Upstate Autumn

by Jed Mannheimer
illustrated by Mark Elliott

Strategy Focus

Melissa and her dad use e-mail to keep in touch. As you read, stop to **evaluate** what happens.

Responding

Think About the Selection

1 How does Melissa feel about her new life?

2 Why do you think computers are so important to Melissa?

3 What clues in the story help you understand why Melissa's dad thinks she's doing great?

Making Inferences

Copy this chart on a piece of paper. Read the clues from the story. Then write what you can infer from each clue.

Clue	What Can Be Inferred
Melissa says that she and her mom actually did something fun.	?
Melissa says being in the library after school is not so bad if Mr. Smitz, Katy, and Tricia are there.	Melissa likes company after school.
Mr. Smitz almost always suggests science fiction books.	?

70

91

December

To: Melissa@eduplace2.com

I can guarantee that you and I will be a twinkling twosome. We can see a musical, maybe with Grandma. I'll be happy to escort you and Kendra around town as we look at the holiday windows. And how about the Bronx Zoo, so you can show me those wood ducks you've been talking about?

To: Dad123@eduplace2.com

I can't wait to see you! Love, Melissa

To: Melissa@eduplace2.com

Ditto, kiddo.

90

September

To: Dad@worldwork.edu

Hey, how have you been? I just set up my new computer. It isn't as cool as yours, but at least it works.

Mom is reading right now. She doesn't seem homesick for the city at all. She seems happy with her new job at the college library. I'm not happy with anything — except how pretty it is up here. You know, we're right on a lake!

But I miss you and my friends. I'm worried about starting school tomorrow. I won't know anyone! E-mail me soon. Love, Melissa

71

To: Melissa@eduplace2.com

Hi Sweetie! Loved your e-mail. Don't worry, I'm sure school will be better than you expect. If I know my girl, you'll have a flock of friends in no time. What's your teacher like?

I just got e-mail at home. I needed a separate address for my personal e-mail. Now it will be easier to stay in touch with you.

To: Dad123@eduplace2.com

My teacher is Ms. Lovejoy. She's okay, but she always goes on and on about outside reading. She wants us to spend all our free time in the library. Maybe if they had computers in the library, I wouldn't mind going.

Actually, maybe you could talk to the librarian, Mr. Smitz, about that. He seems pretty nice. Hey, maybe your company could sell computers to the school at a discount, and then I'd have something to do when I go to the library! Love, Melissa

To: Dad123@eduplace2.com

The book report turned out to be fun, believe it or not. The book Mr. Smitz recommended was awesome! And the report was a snap to write. Work sure is easier when you like what you're doing!

I miss you even more than when I first moved here. I want to know what we're going to do when I visit. There are so many things I want to do! Can we see a musical? I'd like to take a walk around the city and look at the holiday windows. And then see all my friends. And Grandma. But mostly, I want to hang around with you. Love, Melissa

72

89

To: Dad123@eduplace2.com

I told Mr. Smitz about how we e-mail all the time and it reminded him of a book he thought I'd like. And I do. It's about some boy who writes letters to his favorite author. So I finally have something for my book report.

To: Melissa@eduplace2.com

Sweetie, I'll talk to your Mr. Smitz about computers anytime you'd like. I'm not sure about the discount, but do give him my work phone number. And by the way, there's nothing wrong with outside reading, my darling daughter. Or inside reading, for that matter.

To: Dad123@eduplace2.com

Your jokes are so lame! Love you anyway, Melissa

THREE PAGE
BOOK REPORT

74

87

42D

To: Dad123@eduplace2.com

Ms. Lovejoy says we have to write a three-page book report. It's due after Thanksgiving vacation. It's totally not fair! I know for a fact that they only have to write one-page reports at my old school. I guess I could write about ducks, but Ms. Lovejoy said she wants it to be about a book we haven't yet read, and I've read every duck book in upstate New York. Do you have any ideas?

To: Melissa@eduplace2.com

I'm chock-full of ideas, my dear, but I don't know much about books for fifth graders. Ask your Mr. Smitz and see what he suggests. (Just be sure to say, in your most polite voice, "No science fiction, please.")
Love, Dad

86

October

To: Dad123@eduplace2.com

News of the day: Mom and I actually did something fun. When Mom picked me up at the bus stop, she had a brand new pair of ice skates for me. She said the lake will freeze soon. It's not even Halloween yet, but we *are* pretty far north.

Then we went down to the lake. Nobody was there except for the duck family. Did I tell you about them? They are so beautiful — the male has a brown chest, green head, and red eyes! Mom told me they are wood ducks. I ended up watching them all afternoon. Mom took some pictures. I think I'll surf the Net tonight and find out more about them. And just to be fair to books, tomorrow I'll look in the library for what they have. It'll give me something to do when the kids in my class are ignoring me. Love, Melissa

To: Melissa@eduplace2.com

Mel, give those kids another week or so. They're just getting used to having such a gorgeous, smart, and sassy girl in their class. I know what you're thinking — he's just saying that because he's my dad. Honey, I can assure you that I am one hundred percent objective!

75

To: Dad123@eduplace2.com

Columbus Day was fun. In the morning, Mom took me to the library where she works, and then in the afternoon we went skating at the rink with my new friend Katy and her mom. When the lake freezes good and hard, the four of us will be out there slipping and sliding! Sad to say, the ducks won't be around to watch us. They migrate for the winter. Mom says they'll be back next spring.
Love, Melissa

To: Melissa@eduplace2.com

Your dream sounds disturbing. I can understand how something like that can be scary. But you know that no matter what happens, I'll be here, and you will always have a place in the city. Take it easy, and watch out for the fish bones. Much love, Dad

76

85

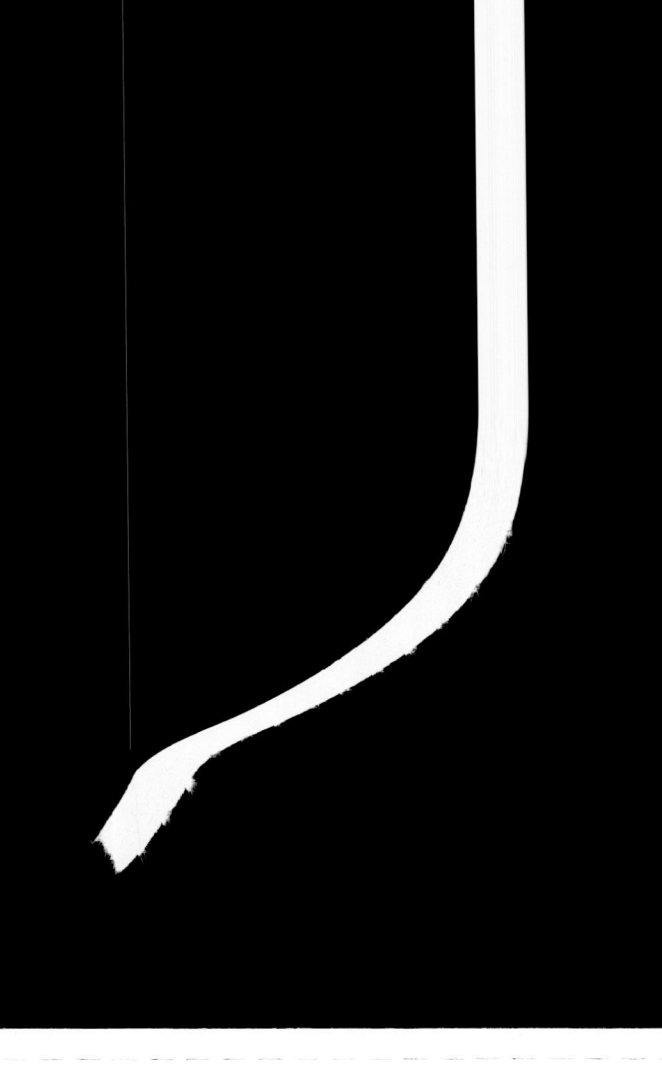

To: Dad123@eduplace2.com

Dinner with Mr. Smitz was okay. We didn't have fish. We had pizza, my favorite. He and Mom didn't talk about librarian stuff, but that would have been boring anyway.

Then I had a nightmare that Mr. Smitz was my stepfather. I would never want him to replace you. I don't think Mom would want him to either. When I told Mom about it, she laughed, but then she said it would be a bad idea to tell Mr. Smitz about it.

To: Melissa@eduplace2.com

Mel, I can't wait to see you in your new skates! We'll skate at Rockefeller Center when you come in for winter break.

Mr. Smitz called me at the office today. He asked me for advice about buying computers for your school. He says they will have the money for a dozen terminals right after winter break! So when I drive you home after vacation, I'll meet with him, the principal, and a couple of teachers. Does that make you happy?

84

77

45D

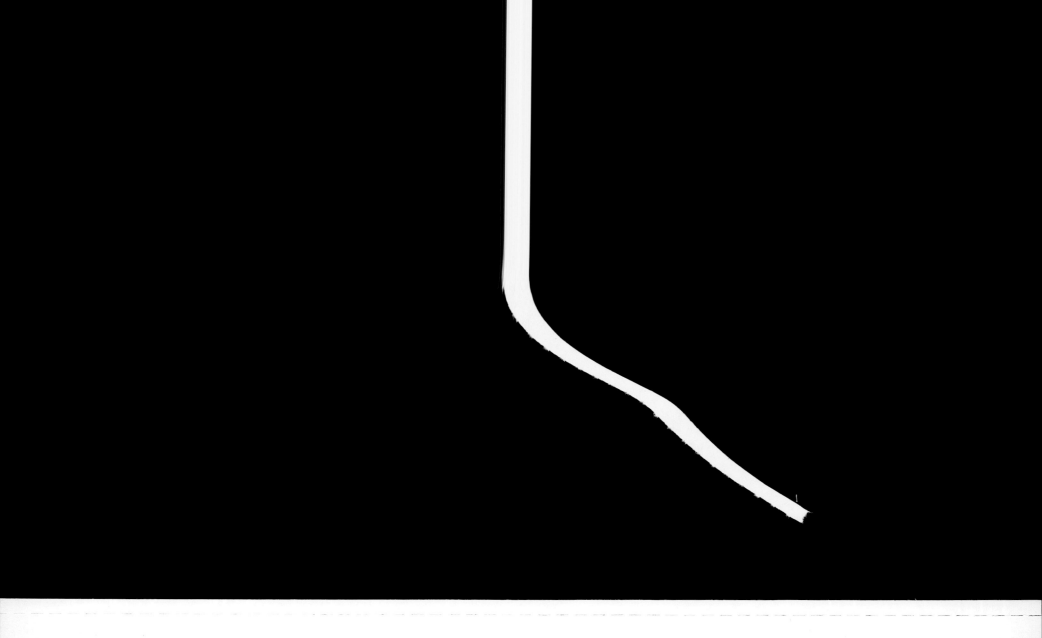

To: Dad123@eduplace2.com

You know that makes me happy. Thanks, Dad.

Now, you're not going to believe this. Mom is just as bad as Ms. Lovejoy. She thinks I should stay at the library after school to do homework. She says that I'm staying up too late getting all my homework done. You know how Mom talks — "You're losing vital sleep and energy."

So from now on, she's going to pick me up at the school library instead of the bus stop. And to make matters worse, we're going to have fish for dinner tonight.

To: Melissa@eduplace2.com

Not much time to write. Sorry about the fish, Shrimp. Do what your mom asks. She actually has your best interests at heart, even though it may not seem so to you at times.

To: Dad123@eduplace2.com

Please don't call me Shrimp. I've grown at least two inches since I saw you.

To: Dad123@eduplace2.com

Mr. Smitz says "Hi." He showed me how to find stuff in the card catalog. I promised I would teach him how to locate books on-line when we finally get computers. He likes deals like that.

I told Mom how nice Mr. Smitz is. I think she's going to invite him over for dinner. I just hope she doesn't make the poor guy eat fish! Love, Mel

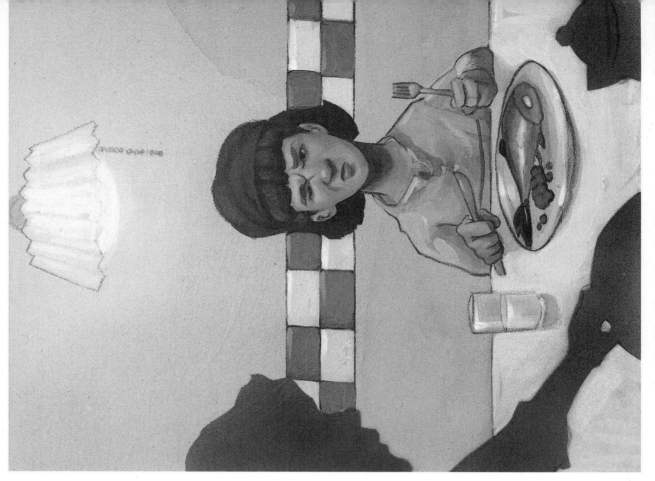

November

To: Melissa@eduplace2.com

I'm sorry that I've been out of touch, Mel. I've been swamped with work and have stayed late at the office almost every night this week! You sound like you're doing great. Mr. Smitz seems like an interesting guy. I'm looking forward to meeting him. I saw your old buddy Kendra the other day. She told me to say "Hi" and that she'd see you during winter break. Your ever-loving Dad

To: Dad123@eduplace2.com

At first I thought Mr. Smitz was kind of slow because he didn't know where the computer books were. It turns out that he's not — he's just totally focused on science fiction. But he likes to talk about *some* other stuff, like nature. He told me that swans stay "married" for life — did you know that?

So it's not so bad in the library after school if he's around. Besides, it's a good place for me, Katy, and our friend Tricia to hang out until our moms pick us up.

To: Dad123@eduplace2.com

Mr. Smitz is having us do volunteer work now. It's fun — all we do is put the returned books on the shelves and listen to Mr. Smitz talk. He tells us about all these weird books that he wants us to read. I told him I don't like science fiction, especially books about computers and robots taking over the world. I think computers and robots will help save the world, don't you? Why haven't you been answering my e-mails lately?

Love, Melissa

48D

HOUGHTON MIFFLIN
Reading
A Legacy of Literacy

One Land, Many Trails

THEME 5

One Land, Many Trails

Reader's Library Selection 1, *Shell-Flower*
To accompany Anthology Selection 1, *A Boy Called Slow*
Comprehension Skill: Drawing Conclusions

Reader's Library Selection 2, *Journey to a Free Town*
To accompany Anthology Selection 2, *Pioneer Girl*
Comprehension Skill: Propaganda

Reader's Library Selection 3, *Zachary's Ride*
To accompany Anthology Selection 3, *Black Cowboy, Wild Horses*
Comprehension Skill: Making Judgments

Reader's Library Selection 4, *America: A Dream*
To accompany Anthology Selection 4, *Elena*
Comprehension Skill: Story Structure

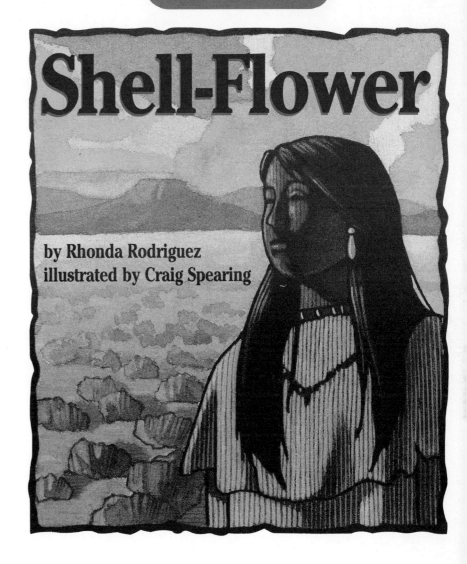

Shell-Flower

by Rhonda Rodriguez
illustrated by Craig Spearing

Shell-Flower

by Rhonda Rodriguez
illustrated by Craig Spearing

Strategy Focus

Can Shell-Flower overcome her fear of the strangers in her land? As you read, try to **predict** how her feelings might change.

4

Responding

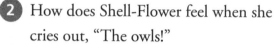

Think About the Selection

1. How does Grandfather act when he hears of the white people's arrival?
2. How does Shell-Flower feel when she cries out, "The owls!"
3. How does Shell-Flower feel about the woman at the end of the story? Why do you think this?

Use Clues — Draw Conclusions

Copy the chart. Then add one conclusion for the second set of details.

Clues from the Story	Conclusions
1. News arrives that white people are coming. 2. People in Shell-Flower's camp run to hide.	The Paiute people are afraid of the white people.
1. Shell-Flower eats the cake. 2. She gets sick. 3. Her father and mother eat the cake and are not sick.	?

25

Several years later, Shell-Flower went to live among white people. She learned to speak, read, and write English. She took an English name: Sarah Winnemucca.

Sarah learned about the ways of white people. She understood that some white people were kind and could be trusted, just as Grandfather had taught. Others were cruel and could not be trusted.

The Northern Paiute suffered as white settlements grew. Sarah Winnemucca tried to do what was best for her people. She spent her life speaking out for fairness, truth, and peace for the Paiute.

24

They came with guns that made lightning and sounded like thunder. They came with hair on their white faces. The white men arrived in Paiute (PIE-yoot) country, and they came like great roaring lions.

Shell-Flower was still a very little girl when the news arrived for the first time: White men were nearby.

Shell-Flower's grandfather was the chief of all the Paiute people. When he heard the news, he jumped up and clapped his hands. "My white brothers!" he cried. "They have finally come!"

5

Grandfather had heard of the white people from far away. He called them his long-lost brothers. He wanted to meet them. Grandfather went to greet the strangers.

Grandfather took a band of men with him. He came to the white men's camp, but they would not meet with him. They turned him away.

Still, Grandfather was filled with hope. He had seen his white brothers for the first time. He returned to Shell-Flower's village and told this story.

In the beginning of the world, there were four children. There was one dark boy, one light boy, one dark girl, and one light girl.

When the children were young, they got along well. But as they grew older, they argued. This made their mother and father sad.

"Why do you argue? You are family," the father said.

The children were ashamed. But there was no peace among them. The parents could bear it no longer.

"If you cannot be good to each other, then you must remain apart," the father said. "Go across the great ocean. Stay out of each other's lives."

The dark girl and boy left together. They went to one side of the ocean. They were the first people of our nation.

6

Shell-Flower turned to see the smile of the woman who had cared for her. The woman bent down and placed a gentle hand on Shell-Flower's face.

Shell-Flower stared up at the woman's face without speaking. It was not the face of an owl. It seemed kind and beautiful. It was like the face of a sister.

It was the face of a friend.

23

The voice said, *"Poor little girl, it is too bad."*

Shell-Flower did not know the meaning, but the sound was comforting. She heard it again and again. *"Poor little girl, it is too bad."* Each time, she felt something touching her face.

At last, Shell-Flower began to feel better. She was able to open her eyes. "Someone from the Spirit World sang to me," Shell-Flower said to her mother and grandfather. She told them about the soft voice and the strange words.

"That voice was not from the Spirit World," said Grandfather. "It was the voice of a good white woman who came to care for you. She put some medicine on your face and spoke kind words to you."

Then Shell-Flower heard the voice again. But this time, the words were different.

"You gave your family quite a scare," said the voice. "That poison oak nearly killed you."

The light boy and girl went to the other side of the ocean. They became the white people's nation.

We have waited all this time for someone to come to us from the white nation, to bring us together again.

22

7

8

8   21

6E

One day, Shell-Flower's brother brought a new food for her to try. It was from the strangers. They called it *cake*. The taste was so sweet that Shell-Flower could not stop eating it. She had never had anything quite like it.

The next day Shell-Flower was sick.

Mother looked at Shell-Flower's swollen face and touched her hot skin. She held Shell-Flower close as she spoke to Grandfather. "Your white brothers gave us food that made my daughter sick," she said.

Shell-Flower could not open her eyes. She heard her grandfather speak to her mother. "I do not think that the cake has harmed her," he said. "I have eaten it, and so have you. No one else is sick."

Shell-Flower's sickness lasted many days.

As she lay with her eyes swollen shut, she heard a soft voice. She felt gentle hands on her face. She remembered what her father had once told her. He had said that a visitor from the Spirit World comes to watch over a sick person. "The voice must be here to take me to the Spirit World," Shell-Flower thought.

Years passed. Grandfather finally met his white brothers. He traveled to their cities in California. He grew to admire and even love his white brothers. Every spring he returned to the Paiute homeland. He told Shell-Flower and her people about the wonders of the white brothers.

"They build houses that can travel," Grandfather said. "Some of their houses travel over the ocean, blown by the wind. They are faster than our horses! Other houses travel across the land on wheels."

One of the white brothers, John Fremont, had given Grandfather a paper. "When we show this to our lost brothers and sisters, it will tell them who we are," Grandfather said. "No harm will come to us when they see it."

For a time, Shell-Flower also longed to meet the white people.

20

9

Then came the awful spring when the Paiutes heard terrible news of the white man. Grandfather was away in California, and Shell-Flower's father was now Chief of the Paiutes. Shell-Flower's father was not as trusting of the white brothers. "They look like owls," he said.

Stories came from other tribes that the white brothers were killing many native people. The adults told Shell-Flower of horrible things that the white brothers were doing.

Shell-Flower was terrified. "How could Grandfather admire such men?" she wondered.

Shell-Flower's father sent his people into the mountains to hide for the winter.

But soon Shell-Flower finally saw the white strangers for the first time. Grandfather brought two white men back to meet the group of travelers. The men smiled at Shell-Flower and bent down to meet her.

"Hide me!" cried Shell-Flower. She ran behind her mother. When the men came even closer, Shell-Flower peeked out. "The owls!" she cried.

Both Grandfather and the white men laughed. The strangers were kind and gentle.

Still, that night, Shell-Flower lay awake, seeing owl eyes everywhere.

The families soon stopped outside of one of the strangers' towns. Grandfather took Shell-Flower's brothers and older sister with him. They came back with wonderful stories of red stone houses and whistling steamboats.

Shell-Flower's brothers had met the strangers. They had not been afraid. Nothing bad had happened.

"Perhaps Grandfather's words are right," Shell-Flower thought.

18

11

9E

Shell-Flower rode behind one of her brothers. They traveled along a river and camped each night. On the third day, some men who had gone ahead came back to the group. "We have seen our white brothers' houses up ahead," they reported.

"Stop here," Grandfather told the group. "I will go to meet them."

Grandfather returned with gifts of food from his white brothers. "I showed them my paper. As long as I have it, we are safe," he said. "We will camp near the white brothers tonight."

Shell-Flower remembered the time she had been buried. This time, she hid under her brother's fur robe. As the horses began to move ahead, she cried against his back.

"Please, let's camp somewhere else tonight," said Shell-Flower's mother. "My daughter is too frightened."

Grandfather agreed. As the group rode by the white men's houses, Shell-Flower kept her head under the robe. She did not want to see.

12

17

But when Grandfather returned, he did not share his son's fear. He now wanted Shell-Flower and her family to come with him to California. He would bring Shell-Flower to meet his white brothers.

The journey to California began in the late fall. Grandfather led many Paiute families. Shell-Flower traveled with her mother, her brothers, and her sisters. Her father remained in the homeland with the rest of the Paiute people.

One day, an alarm passed through Shell-Flower's camp: "The white people are coming!" Everyone began to run.

Shell-Flower's baby sister was strapped on Mother's back. Mother grabbed Shell-Flower's hand. They ran through the camp. Shell-Flower was so afraid, her legs could not keep up. Shell-Flower's aunt also had a small girl who could not run fast enough.

"We must hide our girls!" cried Shell-Flower's aunt.

The two mothers dug holes into the earth. They lowered each girl into a hole up to her neck. They filled the holes with soft soil. They placed sage bushes over the girls' faces to protect them from the sun. "Do not make a sound," said Shell-Flower's mother. "The earth will keep you safe."

Then Mother and Aunt ran off.

16

13

Shell-Flower and her cousin stayed quiet. They did not even whisper to each other. Fear pounded inside them. What if the white people found them?

For hours, Shell-Flower waited for something terrible to happen. Day turned to night.

Then, in the darkness, Shell-Flower heard low voices. Footsteps came close. Shell-Flower's throat closed in terror. "Here. Here they are," said a voice. It was her mother and father! The two children were lifted out of their holes. With Father's arms around her, Shell-Flower slowly stopped trembling.

Shell-Flower would never forget that terrible day. It made her fear the white brothers that Grandfather so loved.

Later that year, other white men destroyed the Paiutes' food and winter supplies. Shell-Flower's father gathered his people and told of a terrible dream he had had. In it, the land of the Paiute was overrun by the white men. Many Paiutes were killed. "To avoid bloodshed, we must all go to hide in the mountains. When my father returns, he will tell us what to do," Shell-Flower's father told his people.

14

15

JOURNEY TO A FREE TOWN

BY DELORES LOWE FRIEDMAN
ILLUSTRATED BY CEDRIC LUCAS

JOURNEY TO A FREE TOWN

BY DELORES LOWE FRIEDMAN
ILLUSTRATED BY CEDRIC LUCAS

Strategy Focus

Will Jake and his family make it to "true freedom" in Kansas? As you read, think of **questions** about the story that you will want to answer by the end.

26

Responding

THINK ABOUT THE SELECTION

1 Why does the author say that the former slaves are not truly free?

2 Why does the man in Hopler's store wait until Jake and Matthew are outside before approaching them?

3 Why is the sign "BEWARE OF INDIANS" an example of propaganda?

IT'S PROPAGANDA

Copy this chart. Then add two details from the advertisement on page 35 that are examples of propaganda.

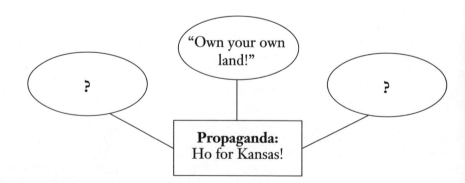

47

One day, when the travelers didn't think they could go any farther, the people in front stopped and pointed up ahead.

"We're in Kansas!" they cried.

In the distance, Matthew saw smoke rising out of small houses. They looked as if they were made of mud.

"Pa, that doesn't look like much," Matthew said.

His mother said, "Don't you worry what it looks like."

Jake added, "We're going to build a free town now. It looks real good to me!"

Everyone smiled. It was time to begin a new life.

46

The Civil War was over. People who once were slaves were now free. However, many of these former slaves were now farming land owned by white men. The farmers had to pay the landowners for rent, seeds, and other goods. Although they were not slaves, they still were not truly free.

Some of the farmers, however, escaped and formed new, independent towns in the West. These towns were also called "free towns." Kansas was one state where these towns were started. This is the story of a family's journey to Kansas — and to true freedom.

27

"Giddyap," Jake yelled, and his old mare looked back. Jake and his son, Matthew, were taking a trip into town.

Jake had been farming cotton in Murfreesboro, Tennessee, for two years, ever since the Civil War had ended in 1865. Every year, he went to town to sell his harvest.

Once he and Matthew arrived in town, they went into Jonah Hopler's general store. Jonah Hopler also owned the land that Jake farmed.

"Morning, Jake," said the man behind the counter.

Pap asked people what work they did. Jake said he had done some blacksmithing. Jake mentioned that Doris could read. Pap smiled and said, "Well, we've got us a teacher too. Are any of you carpenters?"

A couple of young men in the group raised their hands.

"Good gracious, what a fine town you're going to build!" said Pap. As the campfire crackled, other people piped up. One man said he was a doctor. Another knew how to craft leather. All the people would get to use their skills in their brand-new town.

28

45

16E

Matthew looked out on the prairie. He saw only grass and some bare trees near the riverbank. They set up a campfire. Everyone listened to Pap talk about Kansas.

"We've still got quite a ways to go," he said. "When we get there, we'll have to make dugouts. No time to build real houses before winter sets in."

"What's a dugout?" Matthew asked.

"It's a hole in the ground we can use as our home," said Jake. "You'll see."

"Morning, Mr. Hopler. I have this year's cotton crop in the wagon. I'd like to have you price it for me."

Mr. Hopler looked outside and said, "You and your family must've worked pretty hard to get that many bales of cotton in, Jake. Let me just get my book."

Jake didn't have much cash. He had to buy everything — food, clothes, and more — from Hopler. He always paid for it with the money he earned from his crop. Most of the time, Jake left the store still owing Hopler money. This time, however, Jake was sure his crop was so fine he'd be able to sell it, pay the rent, pay for supplies, and still have extra cash to take home.

44

29

"I need some seed for beans, some seed potatoes, and a couple of pounds of corn meal," said Jake. "That ought to do it for today."

Hopler wrote in his book and figured numbers for a long time. Hopler always kept more than careful track of everything Jake owed.

"Jake, you've done real good. You made almost enough to pay what you owe on the land. But you know I had to raise the price this year on the seed. So you owe me three and a half dollars and a few pennies. I'll add the seed and meal. Let's just call it four dollars even," he said with a smile.

Jake's jaw dropped open.

"I don't understand this!" he cried. "I worked hard for that money, all year long!"

"I know it's hard for you to understand, but things cost me, so I've got to charge you," said Hopler.

"I understand one thing. I should have some money left over from all that cotton," said Jake. "I came here because I heard you were fair in paying. Maybe I should find a different piece of land to work."

Matthew froze. What if the Indians attacked? But Pap had no fear. He walked right up to them with a big smile. He talked to them for several minutes in their language. Before they knew it, the Indians had tied pieces of hide to the last wagon, and their horses pulled it up the riverbank. Pap waved thanks as the Indians rode away.

One afternoon, Jake and his family stopped at a sign nailed to a tree. In big red letters, it said, "BEWARE OF INDIANS." As Doris read the words to Jake, Pap came up beside them, shaking his head at the sign.

"Don't believe everything you read," Pap said. "Sometimes the Indians are real helpful to us."

They kept walking. Matthew looked around him once or twice, thinking he might see something passing through the darkness.

After many days, they came to a steep riverbank. The men and women had to work together to push each wagon up. Finally, they were worn out. They could not move the last wagon. While they were resting, they heard horses behind them. They turned and saw six Indians, calmly watching them.

42

31

Matthew couldn't sleep a wink the whole night through. All he could think about was the trip ahead.

The next morning, Pap told Matthew, Lila, and their mother that they would have to get off the boat before it got to St. Louis. The captain said the river up ahead was dangerous, and he wanted to keep the women and children safe.

"Just follow the river, but walk inland," Jake said. "We'll meet you up ahead. By then, we'll be traveling in new wagons that Pap's getting for us."

All the women and children left the boat and started into the woods. A couple of Pap's men went to guide them.

At first, Matthew couldn't see the sky for all the branches in the way. And then, the longer they walked, the fewer trees he saw. They were crossing into the prairie.

Finally, one bright morning, the women and children met up with Jake and the other men. The men were driving six wagons pulled by mules. Lila and the younger children climbed into a wagon. Doris, Jake, and Matthew walked beside them. The group stopped at a creek, filled their water bags, and rested a while. Before long, the journey began again.

41

20E

Hopler scowled, "You better not even think of it, Jake. Now, I know how it is, having nothing to show for all that work. I'm going to loan you a half a dollar so you go home with some money in your pocket."

Matthew noticed a stranger who had been standing in a corner of the store. The man was now listening very closely to the argument. Matthew had never seen him before.

Hopler handed some coins to Jake, saying, "I do the same for you as I do for the other folks that work my land."

Jake took the money without saying a word and started to leave.

"Now, don't let me hear your're planning to farm anywhere but my land next year, Jake. If you leave, I'll come looking for you . . ."

Hopler said his parting words to Jake's back as the farmer walked out the door.

33

As Jake and Matthew walked toward the wagon, the man they had seen earlier quickly walked out of the store and came over to them. He looked serious.

The man handed Jake a small, folded-up piece of paper. "Put this in your pocket," he whispered. He then walked away quickly.

34

Many people were waiting at the landing. They carried their belongings in sacks. They were clustered around a tall, gentle-looking man with silver hair. Many boats, following along the riverbank, passed them by. Finally, one stopped. It was a huge steamboat with paddlewheels on either side of it. Tall chimneys on its deck sent out clouds of black smoke. Matthew was excited. This was the boat that would take them to Kansas!

After Pap talked to the captain and handed him some money, the travelers got on the boat.

39

22E

Later that night, they set out.

The back roads were narrow and full of rocks and tree roots. Jake looked at the stars and pointed out the North Star for Matthew.

Every night, they slept on the ground. Soon Matthew lost track of how many days they had traveled. Before dawn one morning, they reached Nashville, Tennessee.

Jake told Matthew to stay put with his mother and sister while he walked into town to find the man named in the poster, Pap Singleton. When Jake came back, he said, "Folks are meeting upriver at the landing."

Matthew wondered what was on the piece of paper. They climbed into the wagon and drove home. Jake said nothing all the way there.

At home, Jake told his wife, Doris, what had happened. Doris read the paper out loud:

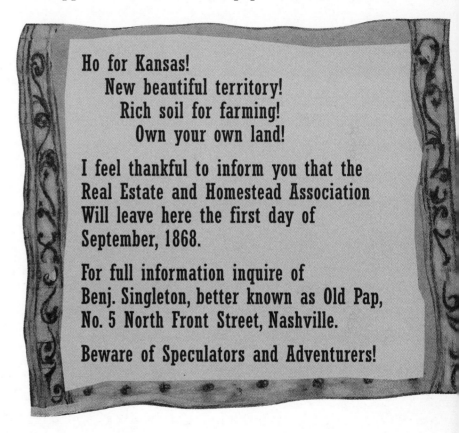

Ho for Kansas!
New beautiful territory!
Rich soil for farming!
Own your own land!

I feel thankful to inform you that the Real Estate and Homestead Association Will leave here the first day of September, 1868.

For full information inquire of Benj. Singleton, better known as Old Pap, No. 5 North Front Street, Nashville.

Beware of Speculators and Adventurers!

"What do you think, Doris?" Jake asked.

"I think we'll always get cheated if we stay here," she said sadly. "I think we should take to the woods — tonight."

38

35

"You sure about this?" Jake asked. "Once we take off, we can't come back. It won't be safe for us. . . ."

"I'm sure," Doris said. "The first thing we need to do is pack our food. Then we pack tools for our crops, and for your blacksmithing. Matthew, you help Pa. Lila, you gather up the food I canned for the winter. We leave after the moon comes up. Like the paper says, Ho for Kansas!"

They took all of their pots, even the big cooking kettle. Jake's wooden plow, along with his hoe, shovel, ax, and tools, went into the wagon too. The last thing they packed was a sack of grain. That was all they had.

"We have to leave as soon as we can get ourselves ready," Jake said. "I don't want anyone to know we're gone until we're long gone. Word might get out to Hopler too soon. "

36

37

Zachary's Ride

by Chenille Evans

illustrated by Beth Peck

Zachary's Ride

by Chenille Evans
illustrated by Beth Peck

Strategy Focus

Can eleven-year-old Zachary do a man's job? As you read, stop now and then to **evaluate** how Zack deals with riding for the Pony Express.

48

Responding

Think About the Selection

1. Why does Zack offer to take the mail?

2. What does Zack mean when he thinks "I didn't think this one out straight"?

3. How do you feel about Zack's leaving his home back east all by himself?

Making Judgments

Copy this chart on a piece of paper. Then complete it to show a judgment you made about Zack. Use this type of chart to make more judgments about Zack.

What the Character Does	What I Think About It	Why I Think This
The stationmaster lets Zack ride to St. Joseph.	The stationmaster should not let a young boy do this.	The ride is dangerous. An adult shouldn't have a boy do this.
Zack decides to make the ride without thinking.	?	?

69

"Nope!" the man answered. "But I'll pay you enough to buy one."

"Pay?" I asked.

"A hundred dollars a month," said the man.

My eyes nearly popped out of my head. I worked the figures in my head. That was twenty times what they paid me at the ranch. Plus, they'd never miss me. "You've got a deal!" I shouted.

"You're hired," said the man. "Now get inside. There's a fire and a bed and some hot grub. Eat up and rest. You've got a long way to go in the morning." He pointed east.

I went inside, warmed up in front of the fire, and had some stew. When I was done, I fell into bed. Before long, I was fast asleep, dreaming of my new life with the Pony Express.

68

It was my day off from doing chores out at the El Dorado Ranch. I was excited about having a full day before me with nothing to do.

It was a beautiful morning. I wandered around Sacramento looking in shop windows and getting the latest news from back east. Out here in California, we were the last folks to get the news. Abraham Lincoln had been elected President! He was a tall, skinny fellow, just like me, except I was only eleven, and he was a full-grown man.

49

    27E

As I walked behind the Pony Express station, I heard whinnying and shouting like I'd never heard before. I ran to see what was going on.

A mustang was snorting and rearing something awful. The stationmaster was trying to calm it down, but he wasn't having much luck. I wondered where the rider was. Then I noticed something, and spoke up.

"Hey, mister, there's blood on this horse," I said, trying to steady the animal.

"Blood? Where?" asked the stationmaster, startled.

I pointed, and he eyed the horse's right side.

"That's blood, all right," he said. A red stream ran down the leather saddlebag on the horse's back and down its dust-coated leg. We looked the horse up and down, but we couldn't find a wound.

"It must be Joe's blood," he mumbled.

He opened the saddlebag. The mail was still inside. The stationmaster breathed a huge sigh of relief.

"Caleb!" the man called to a boy in the cabin. "How soon can you be ready to ride?"

Two minutes later, Caleb and the horse were disappearing in the distance.

The man looked at me. "What's your name, son?" he asked.

I told him, and he said, "Well, Zack, you still have to do better next time if you want the job."

When he saw my surprised look, the man said, "You've got a job if you want one. The run is 75 miles east one day, 75 miles west the next. You change horses every ten miles or so. Think you can handle that?"

"Will you give me a hat and a coat?" I asked.

50

67

28E

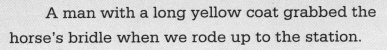

A man with a long yellow coat grabbed the horse's bridle when we rode up to the station.

"Where's Joe?" he asked.

"Missing," I said.

"Well, boy," he said to me, "you're late." He pointed to a fresh horse, as if I were supposed to climb on that one and keep going. "You'll have to do better on the next stretch," he told me.

"Look, mister," I said. "This isn't my job. I did this for fun." I explained what had happened in Sacramento.

66

51

29E

52

65 52

The hail pelted us. I lunged forward to keep the hail off my face and grabbed the horse around the neck. A hundred ice pellets bounced off my back.

The horse was afraid. So was I. I talked to him.

"It'll be all right, old boy. It'll be all right," I repeated over and over again.

I hoped I was speaking truth.

I rode on, clinging to the horse. I tried not to think about anything other than the rhythm of his hooves and my own breathing.

I started to think in spite of myself. I remembered my family back east. I wished I had never gotten on that ship. I wished I hadn't run away. I wished I had never seen California. I wished I had a warm meal and a dry bed. I wished I had a hat. I wished a lot of things.

The hail let up. Then the rain lessened. The horse and I were exhausted. He whinnied as we went around a bend. I guessed that we were nearing the relay point. I soon saw a cabin about half a mile ahead.

"Thank goodness the mail's still here," the stationmaster said. "It came nearly 2,000 miles from Missouri at five dollars a letter!"

I nearly fell over.

"FIVE DOLLARS!" I shouted.

The stationmaster shrugged. "It's a high price, no doubt about that. But those folks back east are just lining up to pay it! We get the mail from here to there or there to here in ten days, sometimes more. It always depends on the weather. It's the fastest way to deliver the mail."

I let out a whistle.

"See here, young fella, I can't talk all day. I've got to find someone to take this mail to the next relay point," said the stationmaster. "I think Bill's got a pony rider there who can get to the station after that."

My heart started beating fast. "I'll do it!" I shouted. "I can ride as good as anyone in these parts. Better, even."

The stationmaster took a good long look at me.

"I won't let you down. I promise," I said.

64

64   53

"You got a name, son?" he asked.

"Zachary," I answered. "But folks call me Zack."

"How old are you?" he asked.

"Old," I said. "Old enough."

"You got family?" was the next question.

"Back east. I've been on my own since I was nine," I answered. It was the truth. I'd been hired as a cabin boy on a ship out of New York. I jumped ship in California and never looked back.

"Then get going," said the stationmaster. "There's a fresh horse tied up by the stable. You've got one hour to get to the relay cabin, you hear?"

Then matters went from bad to worse. Something hit me on the head.

"Ouch!" I shouted. Whatever it was left my head hurting as if I'd been stung by a bee.

It happened again. This time I found the thing that had done it still clinging to my drenched hair. It was a small piece of ice.

Hail.

54

63

When I finally got back on the horse, I was soaked to the skin.

I had already worried about dying of thirst. Now I was fretting about dying from the damp. I had no coat, no hat, not even a decent pair of boots to cover my feet. What had I been thinking?

I rode on, but the rain didn't let up. I was grateful that the horse seemed to know where it was going. I couldn't see two feet in front of my face.

I ran to the horse and swung quickly into the saddle. The stationmaster adjusted the stirrups. He checked the saddlebag filled with mail going east to St. Joseph. It was in order. "It's ten miles out of town," said the stationmaster. "The horse knows the way." Then he added, "I hope."

I was off like a shot. I had no idea where the relay cabin was, but I trusted the horse. After all, Joe's mustang had known the way here.

62

I rode at full gallop. I wasn't sure the horse could keep up this pace the whole way, but I had to get off to a good start. After about ten minutes, my legs started getting sore. I've always been as skinny as a rail, just the sort of rider the Pony Express liked to hire. I didn't have any extra padding to make my ride easier. I slowed the horse to a more reasonable speed, and I felt much better.

56

My mind began to fill with visions of my own death. I had thought I would live to see my twelfth birthday, but now I wasn't so sure. I began to think this ride wasn't such a good idea.

Suddenly the wind picked up and the sky grew black. A crack of lightning ripped across the sky and split a full-grown tree in the trail just ahead of me. The horse reared up. I tried to hold on but I flipped backwards off the horse and into the dust.

I hit the ground so hard it knocked the wind out of me. I saw stars dancing in my head.

The dust I was lying in didn't stay dust for too long. The sky opened up and the rain poured down like a waterfall. I picked myself up and ran after the horse that was jumping around a little way down the trail.

Mud oozed in through holes in the soles of my boots. I slipped and slid all over the place, trying to get hold of the horse and calm him down.

61

Suddenly, I realized I was in the middle of nowhere. There was nowhere all around. Nowhere as far as the eye could see. There were some trees in the distance, but there was no sign that anyone had ever passed through here before.

It made me start to wonder what had happened to Joe. I hadn't given it much thought until now. Had he been attacked by a wild animal? Or had he been shot by an arrow? Or worse?

60   57

I was really alone out there. No one would hear me if I screamed. No one would see me if I were attacked. No one would help me if I were in trouble. All sorts of dangers might be lurking behind the trees and around the corners.

Suddenly, the shadows seemed to have eyes. Was there someone following me? I kept thinking another horse was clip-clopping behind me. I kept going. Did I hear that clip-clop sound again? I spun around. Nothing there. So I rode on and tried not to let my imagination get the best of me.

My throat was parched. I went to grab my canteen but I must have left it at the station in all the excitement. Why didn't I check before I left? What would I do without water? Would I die of thirst?

Would I die of hunger too? Of course, I hadn't brought any food with me. A fellow doesn't just carry food around with him wherever he goes, unless he thinks he'll need it.

"I didn't think this one out straight," I said to myself.

58 59

58 59

AMERICA:
A Dream

by Stanford Makishi
illustrated by José Miralles

AMERICA: A Dream

by Stanford Makishi
illustrated by José Miralles

Strategy Focus

Jiro Akamine came to America with a big dream. As you read, stop every now and then to **summarize** each part of the story.

Responding

Think About the Selection

1 What is Jiro Akamine's dream?

2 Akamine sometimes thinks he was a failure. Do you think he was? Why or why not?

3 In one sentence, tell what you think this story was about.

Story Structure/Summarizing

Copy this map. Complete it by adding the setting, main character, problem, and resolution.

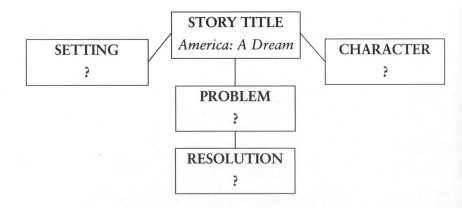

	STORY TITLE *America: A Dream*	
SETTING ?		**CHARACTER** ?
	PROBLEM ?	
	RESOLUTION ?	

90

91

When I was a boy, Japanese people came to America hoping for a better life than we had in our homeland. We all worked very hard. I was luckier than some of the others.

As I write this, I am an old man.

It all happened a long, long time ago. But I still remember when America was only a dream for me.

90

In the late 1800s, people from all over the world were coming to California. They all had a dream of a better life in America. Some of these people, mostly men, came from Japan. This story is about one man, Jiro Akamine. His story is made up from the true stories of many different Japanese men. If Akamine had really lived, he would have told this story when he was a very old man in the 1960s.

71

My family in Japan did not have much money, but we were happy. Our small farm gave us enough to eat. I had many friends. Most of all, I was proud to work with my mother and father on the farm.

As I got older, though, I wanted more for my family. I thought that if I could get an education, I might be able to have a good job someday.

By the time I turned 14, I knew that I would not get the education that I wanted if I stayed in Niigata. I had a cousin and some friends who had gone to find jobs and go to school in California in America.

I made my decision. I would go to America too.

I came to America with one big dream. My dream was to have a good education. No one in my family had finished school, and I wanted to be the first to do it.

When I think about my life in California, though, I realize that perhaps it is better that I did not go back to Japan. Parts of my dream did come true. I did go to school for a time. I found some good jobs. My children got the education I wanted them to have. Even when bad times later came for the Japanese in America, I knew we were here to stay.

Sometimes, I wonder what my life would have been like if I had never left Japan. I imagine I would have worked on my family's farm. Life there would have not been so bad, I suppose.

There were times when I have felt like a failure because I never returned to my family in Niigata. Although I learned to speak English pretty well, I never finished school.

Like some other Japanese people who came to America, my plan was to learn to speak English. I wanted to finish school in America and then go back to Japan. Then, I thought, I could find a good job in my homeland. I was not the only one with this dream.

88

73

41E

I came to California in 1885. I had been on a boat from Japan for days and days. Here I was, finally, in San Francisco.

When I walked off the boat, I realized that I would not return to Japan for a very, very long time. I thought about my family in Niigata. For a moment, I had the terrible thought that I might never return to them.

I didn't really know where to go. But that night, I found my way to a rooming house on Golden Gate Avenue. One of my cousins had told me I might rent a cheap room there.

"Hello, my name is Jiro Akamine," I said to the large man in charge. "I would like to rent a room here." I checked the American coins in my hand. My cousin had sent them to me in Japan. "I have only sixty cents," I said.

Luckily, the large man spoke Japanese. He answered, "We rent rooms for fifteen cents per night. Meals are thirty cents per day."

Over the years, I never made it back to Japan. Shizuko and I raised our family in California when very few Japanese people lived here. During this time, it was often hard to be Japanese in America. We heard stories about fighting between some Americans and people from Japan. There were times when people died in these fights.

However, our family was able to stay safe from this fighting. Shizuko and I were thankful for this, and we did everything we could to make sure that our children had good lives.

Shizuko and I had three children. As they grew older, Shizuko and I decided to move to an apartment of our own. We said a sad good-bye to the Harrises. "You are like a son to me," Mr. Harris said as I shook his hand. "Good luck to you and your family."

On that last day with the Harrises, I think we all wanted to cry.

Even though we stayed in California, Shizuko and I were not American citizens. Back in our day, it was against the United States law for a Japanese person to become a citizen. But our children were American citizens because they had been born here. Our children all went to school. Their English was excellent.

86

75

43E

I thought for a while. I figured out that I could stay there for four nights with the money I had, if I did not pay for meals. I finally said, "Yes, I would like to rent a room for four nights."

"Okay," the man said. "That will be sixty cents, please." I gave him all the money I had.

"Let me show you to your room," the man said with a kind smile.

As we walked up a flight of stairs and then down a dark hallway, I thought about what I had done. I had a place to stay for four nights, but I didn't know how I would eat. I was scared.

I wondered if I had made a mistake in coming to America. I had no money now, and of course I didn't have a job. I spoke only Japanese. When I arrived, very few people in San Francisco spoke Japanese.

76

44E

Of course, compared with some of my friends' lives, my life wasn't so bad. One friend, who worked on a farm in Fresno, died from hunger and sickness. Another friend delivered the Japanese newspaper in San Francisco, but he had to live at the newspaper office and he didn't get paid. At least my job was safe and the Harris family was kind to me. I decided to stay a little longer.

The Harrises helped me with my studies whenever they could. My English improved. And I was enjoying school.

By 1900, wonderful, new things were starting to happen. I was able to get a job as a cook and waiter in a restaurant for ten dollars a week. That year, I also met a woman from Japan named Shizuko, who became my wife.

As it turned out, Shizuko and I moved into the Harrises' house. She cooked and cleaned so that we could live there for free. The Harrises were very kind to her too.

Now I was all alone in a small, dark room. I did not know what to do. I was very tired, though, so I just went to sleep.

84

In the beginning, I could not find work. I found my friends from Japan and borrowed money from them. That way, I could buy food and stay at the rooming house on Golden Gate Avenue. I knew that I had to find a job quickly.

Most of all, I had to stick to my dream of going to school.

After a few hard weeks, I found a job cleaning windows. I slowly started to pay back my friends. Then, at last, I began to study English. I had been in America for nearly two years.

The English lessons were very difficult for me. I had to learn the alphabet, which looked nothing like Japanese writing. And the sounds were very different. I could not always say the words that the teacher taught me.

I studied hard because I had to learn some English before I could get more of an education.

One evening, I just sat in bed after a long day. I was tired and hungry. I had saved about six dollars in two years. My English still was not very good. I wanted to go back to Japan. But I would be ashamed to return without doing what I had come to America to do.

When I thought about my life in Niigata, though, I knew I had no chance of getting a good education there. I would be stuck on my family's little farm for the rest of my life if I went back.

78

83

After working for the Harrises for six months, I was finally able to start making my dream come true.

In the afternoons, I went to school.

After school, I went back to the Harris household to make dinner and do more cleaning. Sometimes, the Harrises sent me home with left-overs. When they didn't, I usually had to skip dinner. On those nights, I just went back to my rooming house on Market Street and slept in my lonely room, hungry. I wondered more and more if I should have ever left Japan.

82

79

47E

Some people who came with me from Japan worked on farms. Others washed dishes, cleaned streets, or worked as delivery people. Whatever we did, we worked hard, and we took whatever pay we could get. Finding a job was not easy for someone who didn't speak English. But we kept trying, because we believed our dreams might come true in America.

After six months, the lessons took hold, and I learned a little English. After that, I was able to get a better job. My new job was cooking and cleaning house for an American family named Harris. I was also able to start school. I moved to another rooming house so that I could be close to the school and my new job.

The Harrises paid me about three dollars a week. In the morning, I made breakfast and cleaned the kitchen. At first, I didn't know what to do in an American house. All I had ever used for eating were chopsticks. The Harrises' forks, knives, and spoons confused me. It took me a while to understand American customs.

80

81

48E

Animal Encounters

HOUGHTON MIFFLIN
Reading
A Legacy of Literacy

THEME 6

Animal Encounters

Reader's Library Selection 1, *The Hyrax of Top-Knot Island*
To accompany Anthology Selection 1, *Grizzly Bear Family Book*
Comprehension Skill: Making Generalizations

Reader's Library Selection 2, *Saving Sea Turtles*
To accompany Anthology Selection 2, *The Golden Lion Tamarin Comes Home*
Comprehension Skill: Topic/ Main Idea

Reader's Library Selection 3, *Kat the Curious*
To accompany Anthology Selection 3, *My Side of the Mountain*
Comprehension Skill: Drawing Conclusions

The
HYRAX
of
Top-Knot Island

by Robin Bernard

photography by
Jerry Lesser

The HYRAX of Top-Knot Island

by Robin Bernard

photography by Jerry Lesser

Strategy Focus

Have you ever seen a hyrax? As you read about hyraxes, **evaluate** how the author tells you about them and where they live.

Responding

Think About the Selection

1. What makes Top-Knot Island different from other islands?

2. Why do you think the author was able to learn so much about the hyraxes and other animals?

3. Why is Top-Knot Island perfect for hyraxes?

Making Generalizations

Several facts can support a single generalization. Copy the web on a piece of paper. Then write information from the story that supports the generalization.

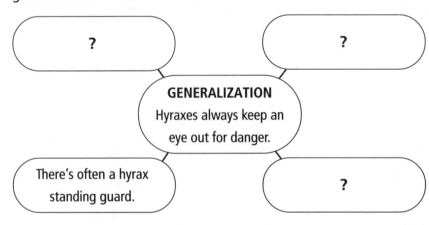

?   ?

GENERALIZATION
Hyraxes always keep an eye out for danger.

There's often a hyrax standing guard.   ?

4

25

2F

Before I knew it, my summer at the kopje was over. When I had arrived, I was only interested in hyraxes. By the time I left, everything on and around Top-Knot Island was special to me. The kopje had become far more than a heap of rocks. It was home for some wonderful creatures, and it offered food to many others as well. But the hyrax would always be my favorite of all the animals I had seen.

I left at sunset. As I drove away, I stole a last look at Top-Knot and said a silent goodbye.

You can't smell the ocean from Top-Knot Island, or hear the splash of waves or the cries of gulls. That's because this rocky island isn't like any other island you've ever seen. It's right in the middle of a sea of grass, on the flat plains of Africa.

Top-Knot Island is really a group of boulders known as a "kopje." Like a real island, it has its own climate, plants, and animals. I went there to study one of those animals, one that most people have never heard of. It's called the hyrax.

24

5

3F

I saw my first hyrax on an earlier trip to Africa. I had climbed some rocks to take pictures of lizards. After a while, I got the feeling I was being watched.

Sure enough, there was a furry little creature looking at me. As soon as I snapped its picture, it ran away.

A moment later it was back. This time it brought along some friends. They all lined up to stare at the two-legged animal with the camera. Maybe it was their funny smiles or bright eyes, but something made me want to find out more about them.

6

As I drove away, I thought about their narrow escape from the leopard. But I figured those cubs would probably survive most dangers. All the things that make hyraxes easy to overlook add to their safety. Their small size and gray-brown fur help them blend in with their background. They have few enemies, and people don't hunt them for food or for their fur. And best of all, hyraxes have the perfect home.

TOM NEBBIA

23

4F

The hyraxes slowly came out of their resting places. As they did, the leopard slowly climbed down the tree. It started moving very quietly toward the kopje. I held my breath.

Suddenly, one of the old male hyraxes sounded the alarm. At almost the same moment, a herd of impalas ran across the grassy plains. The leopard glanced at the kopje once more and then turned and ran after the impalas. After all, impalas were big enough for a feast, not just a snack. I gave a big sigh of relief.

When it started getting dark, I walked back to my car and climbed inside. Just then, two hyrax cubs hopped on the roof. They peeked in at me, and then they jumped off. They ran back to the kopje to play tag on the rocks.

Hyraxes aren't well-known animals. In fact, many people have never heard of them. Maybe that's because hyraxes don't look or act as special as some other animals. Hyraxes don't have graceful horns or beautiful fur. They don't roar or run like the wind. At first glance, they look a lot like big guinea pigs.

Yet to scientists, the hyrax is a very interesting puzzle. Its stomach is like a horse's. Some of its teeth are like a hippo's, some are like a rhino's, and some are like a rodent's.

22

7

But if you ask scientists to name the hyrax's closest relative, they will tell you it's the elephant. Clearly, hyraxes don't look anything like elephants. But their front leg bones, feet, and brains are a lot like an elephant's.

Hyraxes and elephants are also alike in other ways. Most mammals that are as small as hyraxes give birth to their babies in about eight weeks. But a hyrax mother needs seven and a half months to have babies. An elephant mother also takes a long time to give birth.

PETER DAVEY

When the rhino finally left, I climbed down to my car to get my lunch. Just as I finished eating, I thought I saw something move in a thorn tree. I looked more closely. I found a pair of yellow eyes staring back at me.

It seems that I wasn't the only one eager to see the hyraxes again. A long, lean leopard was stretched out on a nearby tree limb. He waited and watched. He looked as if he was ready for a hyrax snack.

8

21

During the midday heat, hyraxes rest in their cool dens. When I was watching them, I took my lunch break while they rested. But one afternoon it looked as if lunch would have to wait a while. Standing at the foot of Top-Knot was a handsome, very large rhino! He was so close, I could see every fringe on his ears. Luckily, he didn't notice me.

CAROL HUGHES

Hyraxes and elephants have something else in common, too. They both have trouble cooling down.

Elephants can dunk themselves in a river or pond. They can also flap their ears to cool off.

Hyraxes try to keep cool by living on a kopje. If they get too warm, they can go into the shady spaces between the rocks. Top-Knot even has a cave where the air never gets too warm.

ROBERT GILL

20

9

Adult hyraxes hardly ever sniff each other face to face. If they do, they usually end up fighting.

But hyraxes have more to worry about than elephants do. That's because hyraxes are small enough to make an easy meal, while elephants are not.

So hyraxes always keep an eye out for danger. There's often a hyrax standing guard on one of the kopje's highest boulders. From there he can spot a hungry eagle a mile away. He also watches the grass for prowling leopards, who are very fond of hyrax "snacks."

If the hyrax guard sees anything dangerous, he gives a high whistle. The alarm sends the whole hyrax colony diving into the deep, dark spaces between the rocks. In seconds, there's not a hyrax to be seen.

10

The adults spend most of their time fanned out or resting back to back. Lying that way helps the hyraxes in two ways. First of all, it helps prevent fights, because the hyraxes are facing away from each other. Second, facing out means they can see in many directions. That gives the hyraxes a better chance of spotting any enemies.

19

Like most mammals, hyrax cubs greet each other by sniffing. I watched them do this over and over again. After sniffing, one hyrax ran a short way off and looked back at me. It seemed to be asking, "Are you ready to play?" Cubs often go nose to nose with adult hyraxes, too. The grown-ups nuzzle them for a moment, and then give them a gentle shove toward their playmates.

The kopje offers more than protection to the hyrax. It offers something else that's just as important — food.

In Africa's dry season, the sun beats down and there is very little rain. The grass that covers the plains often turns brown and dies. But green plants almost always grow on Top-Knot. Morning dew collects on the rocks and then trickles into the soil. Then it's soaked up by plant roots.

18   11

Top-Knot's green plants attract many fur-covered and feather-covered visitors.

One morning while I was watching the hyraxes eat their breakfast, I saw two giraffes picking their way along the lower rocks of the kopje. The hyraxes seemed as surprised as I was to see the giraffes there.

The giraffes stretched their long legs and long necks and stuck out their long tongues, but they still couldn't reach the leaves they wanted. After a while, the giraffes gave up and went off. All of Top-Knot's greenery is easy for hyraxes to reach, because they can scamper up and down the rocks.

The hyraxes grew used to having me around. If I just sat quietly, they nibbled flowers and leaves right near me. One day, when a female hyrax came very close to me, I saw something I hadn't noticed before. She had a few long hairs evenly spaced along her back. They were stiff, just like a cat's whiskers. Later, I found out that the hairs are used as "feelers." In caves and dark spaces between the rocks, these special hairs are like extra hands that help hyraxes "feel" where to go.

12

17

During the summer I spent studying the hyraxes, I found out a lot about their habits. For one thing, I learned how some hyrax cubs get so good at climbing rocks. They practice by jumping onto their mothers. Then they may climb up her back and reach her neck. Finally, they may get all the way up to the top of her head.

I saw one cub hop onto his mother's back many times every day. He jumped up easily, but getting down was another matter. Each time he jumped off his mom, he got better at it. In a few more days, he became very good at climbing on hyraxes. Then he was able to climb up and down the rocks easily.

After the giraffes left, the hyraxes kept munching away on their morning meal. A few minutes later, I heard squeaks and squeals right below me. Pygmy mongooses! They wiggled, jumped, and rolled over. Finally, one stopped long enough for me to take its picture.

Just knowing these snake-killers lived on the kopje made me feel safer. I hadn't met a deadly snake yet, and I hoped I never would. Their poison can kill someone almost instantly.

16

13

The cubs inched closer and closer to me. They came so near I could almost reach out and touch them. Just then, their mom decided they were getting too nosy. She gave a soft call, and immediately the cubs ran back to her side.

It was a good thing she called them. I knew that people should never touch wild animals, but those fluffy cubs were very hard to resist.

The next day, three tiny hyraxes appeared at the kopje. They looked more like puppies than African wild animals. I didn't spot their mother right away, but I knew she must be nearby. Aha! There she was, on a ledge just a few yards away, watching every move her babies made.

14

15

SAVING SEA TURTLES

by Amy Edgar   illustrated by Tom Leonard

SAVING SEA TURTLES

by Amy Edgar   **illustrated by Tom Leonard**

Strategy Focus

Will sea turtles disappear? As you read the story, stop now and then to **monitor** how well you understand the turtles' problems, and reread to **clarify**.

26

Responding

THINK ABOUT THE SELECTION

1 What kind of sea turtle is most likely to disappear?

2 What has hurt the Kemp's Ridley sea turtle?

3 What is the main idea of this story? (Reread page 45.)

TOPIC, MAIN IDEAS, AND SUPPORTING DETAILS

Copy the chart on a piece of paper. Fill in the topic, one main idea, and a supporting detail for each main idea.

Topic: _____?_____

Main Ideas	Supporting Details
?	• A land turtle can pull its head in, but a sea turtle can't. • ?
People are trying to save sea turtles.	• Scientists and volunteers protect sea turtle eggs. • ?

47

14F

Can a creature that outlived the dinosaurs survive in our world? Only time will tell.

INTRODUCING SEA TURTLES

Sea turtles have lived on Earth since the days of the dinosaurs. Scientists think they may be related to crocodiles and even birds.

Three Kinds of Sea Turtles

Hawksbill   **Kemp's Ridley**   **Loggerhead**

There are seven kinds of sea turtles. All of them are endangered. The Kemp's Ridley sea turtle is the closest to extinction. In 1947, 40,000 Kemp's Ridley sea turtles laid eggs on a single day. In 1998, only 2,000 of them laid eggs in an entire year.

Why are there so few left today? One answer is that we have harmed both the turtles and their natural habitat. Scientists are afraid that Kemp's Ridley sea turtles might soon disappear from the oceans forever.

46   27

FEATURES OF SEA TURTLES

Sea turtles are like land turtles in some ways. They are also quite different. A land turtle can pull its head inside its shell to hide from danger. A sea turtle cannot. Instead, it swims away from danger. A land turtle has feet and claws for walking. A sea turtle has flippers for swimming.

land turtle   **Kemp's Ridley**

Sea turtles are the fastest swimmers of all animals with four legs. Some have been recorded swimming as fast as 20 miles per hour. A sea turtle's flippers are shaped like paddles. It swims by moving its two front flippers — like a bird flapping its wings. At the same time, it steers with its back flippers. No one knows for sure how deep sea turtles go when they dive and swim.

For now, the Kemp's Ridley sea turtle is still in serious danger. However, there is reason for hope. Over the last five years, the number of nests counted in Mexico and Texas has gone up. In 1995 only four nests were found on Padre Island. In 1998, 13 were found.

28

45

WHAT WILL HAPPEN TO THE KEMP'S RIDLEY SEA TURTLE?

Scientists hope that protecting the hatching and release of Kemp's Ridley sea turtles will help their numbers to grow. They also hope the hatchling turtles will return to Padre Island to nest when they are adults. Whether this will happen or not is still a mystery.

A Kemp's Ridley sea turtle is smaller than other sea turtles. It is about two feet long with a dark green-gray shell and skin. The average weight of a Kemp's Ridley sea turtle is 100 pounds. The average weight of a Leatherback sea turtle is 1,000 pounds.

Leatherback

Kemp's Ridley

44

29

Sea turtles need to breathe air. Their lungs remove every bit of oxygen from the air that they breathe. That way they can stay underwater for a long time. Active turtles swim to the surface for a breath every few minutes. Resting turtles can stay underwater for up to two hours. When it is time for a turtle to sleep, it sinks to the bottom of the ocean. There the water is colder and less oxygen is needed to breathe.

BACK ON THE BEACH

On the beach, volunteers stand near the shore. They guard the baby sea turtles as they crawl out of the box. Two boys chase away some sea gulls and a crab that might have harmed the hatchlings. One baby sea turtle begins to go the wrong way, away from the ocean. A girl picks it up and gently places it in the water. In a flash, it swims off to its new life in the ocean.

That life will be a hard one. Baby sea turtles have many enemies in the ocean. They may be eaten by a large fish or crab, swallow the plastic top from a juice container that was carelessly tossed away, or drown in a net. Scientists believe that only 1 out of 100 hatchlings survives to be an adult turtle.

A sea turtle never chews its food, because it doesn't have any teeth. Instead, it crushes its prey with its powerful jaws. Its jaws are so strong that it can crush just about anything, even tough clam shells. A Kemp's Ridley sea turtle eats mostly fish and shellfish. Two of its favorite foods are crabs and jellyfish.

A sea turtle lives its life alone in the ocean. Only the female sea turtle ever returns to land. Here's what happens when a Kemp's Ridley sea turtle returns to lay her eggs.

42

31

A SEA TURTLE RETURNS TO LAND

The scene is a windswept beach on Padre Island, Texas. A Kemp's Ridley sea turtle struggles onto the shore. She hasn't been on land since she was a baby turtle, a hatchling.

The sea turtle is graceful and speedy in the water, but she is clumsy and slow on land. She drags herself over the sand with her flippers. Soon she reaches a part of the beach that is safely above the high tide mark. Using her back flippers, she begins to dig a hole in the sand.

Finally, the turtles start hatching and moving about in the nesting hole. The hatchlings work together to dig their way out of the sand.

The scientist counts and weighs the baby turtles. Then he calls volunteers and tells them to meet him at the beach where they discovered and collected the eggs.

32

41

AT THE LABORATORY

Back at the science laboratory, the eggs are gently buried in a hole just like the one the mother turtle dug for them. Then the waiting begins. It will be about fifty days before the baby turtles begin to hatch. The scientist will watch over the eggs, making sure that they don't get too hot or too cold.

When the hole is deep enough, the sea turtle starts to lay her eggs. One after another, the soft, round eggs drop into the hole. They look a little like Ping-Pong balls. When she finishes, she covers them with sand. Then she slowly makes her way back to the water and swims out to sea.

Her eggs will hatch in about fifty days, but she won't be around to greet her babies. Turtle babies aren't like human babies. They don't need their parents' help to survive. They are born knowing how to find their way into the ocean. They are also born knowing how to swim. But they have to struggle to stay alive.

THE STRUGGLE TO SURVIVE

The survival of sea turtles is threatened by humans in many different ways. Shrimp boats drag huge nets to catch shrimp. Some sea turtles also get caught in the nets. Sea turtles are hunted for their skin, shells, and meat. Wallets, jewelry, and soup made from sea turtles are still being sold in some parts of the world.

Soon the scientist arrives to dig up the turtle eggs. He counts them. Then he carefully places them in a box. He also puts some sand from the nesting site into the box. He hopes that burying the eggs in that sand will help the turtles come back to the same beach when they are adults.

In his notebook the scientist writes down the number of eggs, how deep the nest is, the time of day, and the weather. Then he marks the nesting site with a pole. He will return to it with the baby turtles when they are ready to be released into the ocean.

SCIENTISTS STEP IN

Some scientists and volunteers help to protect sea turtle eggs. They also protect the baby turtles when they hatch.

First, a volunteer spots turtle tracks leading down to the water. Those tracks show that a female sea turtle has left her eggs nearby. The volunteer beeps the scientist who is on duty. Then the volunteer watches the area around the turtle tracks until the scientist arrives. As he watches, a gust of wind might come along and blow away the turtle tracks. But because the volunteer has been watching closely, the scientist can still find the eggs when he gets there.

People living near beaches are also a threat to the survival of sea turtles. Humans can crush sea turtle eggs by accident as they play at the beach. Pollution also kills sea turtles. They often swallow things like plastic bags. The bags may look like jellyfish to the turtles. The plastic can choke them. Or it can keep them floating at the surface of the water, unable to dive for food.

38

35

PROTECTING SEA TURTLES

Some people are concerned about the fate of sea turtles. They are taking action to save them. A Turtle Excluding Device (TED) was invented so that people can fish for shrimp without trapping turtles. The TED lets turtles escape the fisherman's net. Sadly, many people are not willing to use TEDs when they fish for shrimp.

They say the TEDs cost much more than regular nets and are harder to use.

Others are doing their best to help turtles that nest on beaches where many people go. A hotel in Palm Beach, Florida, has a boardwalk that leads to the beach. It helps prevent guests from disturbing the eggs that may be buried there.

KAT
THE CURIOUS

by Barbara Brook Simons

illustrations by Patrick Faricy

KAT
THE CURIOUS

by Barbara Brook Simons
illustrations by Patrick Faricy

Strategy Focus

Where will Kat's curiosity lead her? As you read, stop at important points in the story to **summarize** what has happened.

48

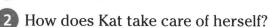
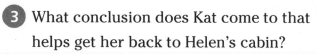

Think About the Selection

1. Why does Kat get lost?

2. How does Kat take care of herself?

3. What conclusion does Kat come to that helps get her back to Helen's cabin?

Use Clues – Drawing Conclusions

One way to think about drawing conclusions is to keep a chart like this. Copy the chart on a piece of paper. Then complete the chart.

What Kat Knows	Kat's Conclusions
Kat knows raccoons wash their food.	If she follows a raccoon, it will lead her to water.
She can eat the same kind of food as a raccoon eats.	?
Squirrels know where to get nuts.	?

69

Aunt Helen was on the porch. When she saw me, she started to cry. "You're safe, you're safe! The state police are looking all over Fox Cliff! Why did you wander off like that? I must have gotten home just minutes after you left."

"I was just curious," I said. "I thought I knew the way. I'm really sorry I worried everybody."

"Kat the Curious," Aunt Helen said. "No more exploring on your own! Next time you get curious, I'm coming with you! Now what is that raccoon doing on the porch?"

68

I didn't plan to get lost. Actually, I was never *really* lost. I was just — you know, curious. I'm sorry I scared everyone, though. I guess the only person who wasn't scared was me! Here's what happened.

49

I was going to spend a week with Aunt Helen while my parents went camping in the Rocky Mountains. I should tell you that Helen is not my *real* aunt. She's an old friend of my mother's, and since she has no children of her own, she's kind of adopted me as her niece. She has a little log cabin on a hilltop in the woods, with a big stone chimney and a great view.

We went on that way for at least an hour. Then things began to look familiar. Suddenly, we came out of the woods—and there was Aunt Helen's cabin only a few yards away. Bandit scurried around the corner to the garbage can.

50

50 67

Did Bandit understand me? I'll never know. Maybe he just knew that this was his world, and I didn't belong in it. In any case, he started off through the woods. It looked as if I should follow him, so I did.

Following Bandit, I saw how lost I was. I was nowhere near Fox Cliff. If people were looking there, they wouldn't find me. Bandit trotted quickly through the woods. I could see a faint path, not one made by people. Maybe it was the path that deer and other animals made when they went to the stream.

The cabin is only about forty miles from a city, but it feels farther away than that. I guess that's because Aunt Helen has no electricity or phone line. We use kerosene lamps and candles. (Aunt Helen does bring her cell phone for emergencies—she's not *that* much of a pioneer.)

My parents and I left home very early that morning, and we got to the cabin at about 2:30. Aunt Helen expected us at around three, so we were a little early. Sure enough, she wasn't home. (Aunt Helen is hardly *ever* home unless she has to be.)

66

57

Hi folks!
In case you get here
early, I've gone to town
for some of that cheddar
cheese that Kat likes.
I'll be back before three.

Anyway, there was a note on the door that said, "Hi, folks! In case you get here early, I've gone to town for some of that cheddar cheese that Kat likes. I'll be back before three."

I saw my dad looking at his watch. "Why don't you guys take off?" I said. "I'll be fine, and Helen will be back soon. And if I really want to get in, I know how to go through the kitchen window. Don't worry about me. Have a great time!"

I must have been pretty convincing. After many good-bye hugs, they left.

I was nibbling some grapes when Bandit poked his nose around the corner. "Do you want some grapes, Bandit?" I asked, as I put a few on the ground. He picked them up with his paws, which looked just like little hands. "You like people food, don't you, Bandit? Was that you in Aunt Helen's garbage can yesterday?"

52

65

The next morning I woke up early, with a squirrel scolding me. "Sorry, the peanut butter cookies are all gone," I said. "It's your turn to get breakfast. How about some nuts? Fruit? Cornflakes?" The squirrel ran up a hill toward some small trees. Round brown nuts hung from the branches.

"Hazelnuts!" I said. I'd never seen them growing before. Somewhere I'd read that the Winnebago Indians loved hazelnuts. Before they get ripe, the nuts are supposed to be soft and sweet. I smashed a shell, tried one, and found that it was true.

When I'd had my fill, I looked around. Through the oak trees, I saw the shape of a house! I climbed through spiky bushes toward it. When I got close, I saw that the house was a ruin with only one wall. Wild grapevines twisted over it.

64

I sat on the porch steps. The air smelled of warm grass and sweet clover. The last thing I wanted was to be inside. I just wanted to sit and listen to the sounds of nature. After all, I'd been listening to city noises all year. (Talk about ear pollution . . . !)

A warm breeze rustled the tops of the trees, and grasshoppers chirped in the tall, purple-flowered weeds. A loud "rat-tat-tat" told me that a woodpecker was drumming on a nearby tree.

53

32F

63

Soon it was time to make camp. I'd had a long day, and I was awfully tired. I searched for a rocky overhang to lie under. That way, if it rained the overhang would keep me dry. Then I used my knife to cut some long green saplings, and I propped them against the rocks. I wove in thin branches to make a framework, and I draped my sweatshirt over it, making a kind of tent.

It was getting pretty dark. I wasn't scared—not really, anyway. There aren't any dangerous animals like bears or wolves in southern Wisconsin. I had a flashlight, but a fire would be nicer. "Wait a minute," I said to myself. "I took this backpack the last time I went camping. Maybe I still have that tin of matches." I did—six precious matches. I had to use two of them to light a fire.

The glow from the fire danced on the rocks behind me. Spring peepers cheeped in the trees. Big frogs rumbled in their bass voices.

I curled up on a bed of soft, dry grass and sweet-smelling pine needles. My extra sweater made a pretty good blanket. I watched the stars until I fell asleep.

Suddenly I heard a rustling noise behind the cabin, where Helen kept the garbage can. Maybe a raccoon was looking for a snack.

That reminded me that I was hungry. I was unwrapping a sandwich when a chipmunk ran along the porch railing. It stopped and flicked its tail, and I gave it a bit of sandwich.

After I finished eating, I began to get impatient. Where *was* Aunt Helen? I'd come all this way to enjoy the woods, and I couldn't wait any longer. I was dying to see my favorite places again.

I saw a flash of color in the trees and said, "What *is* that bird?" That's when I knew I had to go explore — right now. I knew these woods very well and was certain I could find my way.

62

55

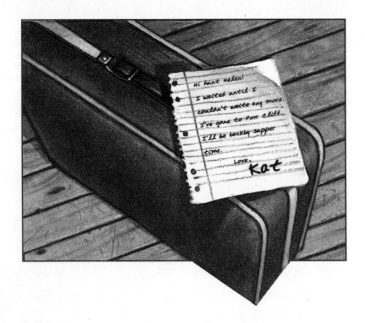

I wrote a note on a page from my notebook. It said, "Hi Aunt Helen! I waited until I couldn't wait anymore. I've gone to Fox Cliff. I'll be back by suppertime. Love, Kat."

I put the note on top of my suitcase. Then I put on my backpack and walked into the shady woods.

Under the trees, the air was cool and fresh. As I headed for Fox Cliff, sunlight shone through the leaves, making small, dancing patterns on the ground. I should mention that Fox Cliff is a bluff of carved sandstone near the river. I'd been there a hundred times. Well, maybe more like nine or ten times, to be truthful.

As I filled my water bottle, I looked at the shallow water at the edge of the stream. A bright green plant was growing there. Watercress! I picked handfuls of the spicy leaves for a wild salad.

The raccoon had already finished his dinner. He didn't seem to be afraid of me at all. He looked up at me through his black mask.

"Okay, Bandit," I said. The name just seemed to fit. "What do you eat that I can eat?" He trotted up the bank to a tangle of bushes loaded with small reddish fruit—wild plums. Bandit was inviting me over to his place for dessert!

56

61

I looked in my backpack. I had a little food—half a sandwich, an apple, and some chips—a flashlight, and a knife. I had warm clothes, too. What I needed was fresh water. A little more to eat would be nice, but it wasn't necessary.

Something moved in the bushes. I sat very still while a raccoon with something in his mouth scurried past. I remembered that raccoons wash their food, so I scurried after it. He led me right to a spring bubbling out of a crack in a rock.

Acorns crunched on the path under my feet. The noise startled two squirrels, who jumped to a branch over my head. I tossed bits of peanut butter cookie toward them. They ran down the tree and scampered off with the crumbs. Then they followed me, hoping they'd get some more.

They kept up with me as the trail twisted and turned. When I passed a huge hollow tree, they jumped into it and watched me go on my way.

60

57

I continued on the trail, making all the turns I remembered. Pretty soon, I thought, the path would wind uphill. Then the woods would open out, and I'd be at the cliff. "Funny," I said to myself. "I didn't remember it was this far. I've been walking for a long time."

Suddenly, nothing looked familiar. I came to another fork in the path and knew that I had no idea which way to go.

I chose one path and started down it. I was really lost. The trees' shadows were getting longer, and my watch said it was getting late. I couldn't possibly get back to the cabin in the dark — even if I knew the way.

It was then that I realized I would have to spend the night in the woods. I wasn't really worried. In fact, I thought it was kind of exciting. But I knew Aunt Helen would be out of her mind with worry, and I felt bad about that.

58

59